L.

Chunnel

chunnel

everyman's guide to the technicalities
of building a channel tunnel

by **C. A. PEQUIGNOT**

CR BOOKS LIMITED
The Adelphi, John Adam Street, London W.C.2
1965

FIRST PUBLISHED 1965

©
C. A. Péquignot

Set in 11 point Monotype Imprint on 12 point body and made and printed in
Great Britain by F. J. Parsons Ltd. of London, Folkestone and Hastings

Preface

MOST GREAT constructional and civil engineering works are done in the light of day. What pedestrian has never stopped to look down into the hole in the road or peer through a crack in the board fence, just to see what's going on?

Bridges and roads, dams and power stations, sewage works, docks and sea walls, great office blocks, schools and hospitals, multi-storey car parks—these do not appear overnight. So Mr Everyman on his way to work or even when touring on holiday has ample opportunity to see all these modern wonders in all their stages of construction. And what he misses seeing for himself, the press photographers put before him on his breakfast table.

Our Mr Everyman acquires a pretty sound idea of what goes on, and if there are any gaps in his understanding the cinema and television documentaries soon put him wise.

But what of tunnelling? It is perhaps the earliest activity of human beings to be recognizable as civil engineering, yet who has seen it going on except the tunnellers themselves? The circumstances in which men burrow beneath the ground do not lend themselves to photography—even less to the television camera. So Mr Everyman lacks the long series of visual impressions, linked together by the public explanations, which have made him almost an expert on every other kind of construction. So when, on the few occasions that the Channel Tunnel is mentioned in the press or in radio programmes, he is at a disadvantage. Such discussions are necessarily short. And yet it is one of the most vital topics of the century. So the snippets of technical gen which do get through can give only a shallow comprehension of why this inspiring project has taken a hundred and fifty years to be accepted by authority as feasible.

It is the aim of this book to give, in simple language, some digestible information about the secret arts which are practised so largely out of sight, and to bring the engineering problems of the Channel Tunnel out of the realms of science fiction into the everyday vocabulary of all who like to natter about this and that over a pint in the pub or in the corner seat of the 8.17.

Little in this book is new. Nearly all of it has been said before, somewhere or other. But previous writings on the technicalities of the Channel Tunnel have been aimed at the engineer who is familiar with the basic principles; whilst several excellent books for the layman have concerned themselves too lengthily with history and finance to leave room for a sufficient explanation of the part which engineering has played in making the history so long and the economics so complex.

It is not, then, a book for civil engineers to read; there is already ample technical literature for them. It will tell the historians little; for the history has been fully and entertainingly told elsewhere. It holds nothing for the traffic statistician; few but the statisticians will believe statistics anyway, so none are included. It is not a book for the lawyer, the accountant, the financier, or the politician who confine their reading to their own respective disciplines, for the author knows little of the aspects which would interest such specialists, except that they cannot be discussed in simple language.

Who is left? Perhaps you, who have been patient enough to read so far. If you admit to being in none of the categories "warned off"—that is, if you admit to being Mr Plain Man, it may be that you will find something in the following pages that will make you feel less vulnerable when your children ask questions.

C.A.P.

Acknowledgements

I AM particularly grateful to Mr. Ian Ogilvie, who has made many useful suggestions and, after reading the MS, many more, all of which have been incorporated.

M. Réné Malcor, Ingénieur en Chef des Ponts et Chaussées, Delegate of the Channel Tunnel Study Group, has also honoured me by reading the MS, and in those parts which related to the aspects of the Study Group's work for which he is responsible, he made some suggestions which I have been glad to incorporate.

I am obliged too to the following firms who have supplied the originals of illustrations and/or given permission for them to be published:

Distington Engineering Co. Ltd., Workington	Fig. 7(c)
Eimco (Great Britain) Ltd., London ...	Fig. 7(a)
Lawrence Machine and Manufacturing Inc., Seattle	Figs. 17, 18
Mitchell Bros., Sons & Co. Ltd., London ...	Fig. 11
Mott, Hay and Anderson, London	Fig. 10(b)
Edmund Nuttall Sons & Co. (London) Ltd.	Figs. 8(a), 9
Robert L. Priestley Ltd., Gravesend ...	Figs. 8(a), 9, 11
James S. Robbins & Associates, Seattle ...	Figs. 14, 16
Smith Tool Company, Compton, California	Fig. 18

and to Mr. S. C. Sargent, of Cape Girardeau, Missouri, for Fig. 15 and Mr. J. Weaver of Cement & Concrete Association for Fig. 55; and to Mr. R. H. Falkiner of Edmund Nuttall, Mr. H. A. McClunie of Eimco, Mr. A. C. Twort of Binnie & Partners, Mr. W. W. Watkins of Lawrence Machine, Mr. J. Whattler of Robert L. Priestley, and many of my office colleagues for their general helpfulness.

C.A.P.

Contents

PART THREE

THE END OF AN ADOLESCENCE—*which
means to say that the comparatively new technique
of tunnelling by laying prefabricated tubes in a
submarine trench is now an established practice*

PART FOUR

STOP PRESS

PART ONE

Once upon a time

which is basic English for a "résumé of the various proposals for a Channel Link"

CHAPTER ONE

Genesis

or the birth of an idea

VISIONS

THE PROSPECT of a transport link between Britain and the Continent has fired the imagination of engineer and layman alike for more than 150 years. The story of the Channel Tunnel during those years is a composite saga of hope and frustration, enthusiasm and dejection, political intrigue and military stubbornness, technical wizardry and pipe-dream unreality; but mainly it is a story about two periods (perhaps the two longest in history) during which two nations have continuously failed to say in unison "Let's go!" and "En avant!"

There was a break in this miserable tale when, in 1875, there was sufficient "togetherness" between the engineers, politicians, and military of Britain and France to permit the starting of exploratory tunnelling works. The fever lasted but eight years, then the God of Frustration was re-enthroned for his second long reign, characterized by all the same epithets.

The Channel Tunnel story really begins in 1802, and for the next 100 years or so it is a biographical tale of men; of engineers who were visionaries; of visionaries who were not quite engineers; and of men who were neither—this includes monarchs, politicians, financiers, clergymen, doctors and, of course, the backbone of all reactionary stubbornness, the top brass of the army.

The tale has been told in a fascinating and exciting manner by Slater and Barnett*. It would be impertinent to those authors to give here any more than a brief whetting to the reader's appetite for history.

---

*Humphrey Slater and Corelli Barnett, "The Channel Tunnel." Wingate, London, 1958.

The years 1802 and 1803 present the charcoal skeleton of a picture which has been painted in brighter colours in the early 1960's. The rivalry between two entirely different methods which existed unwittingly in 1802/3 has now assumed a sharper focus. It was in the first of those prophetic years that the Frenchman, Albert Mathieu proposed to Buonaparte that a tunnel 15 kilomctres long could be driven from each side of La Manche to the Varne Bank—a ridge on the sea-bed—where Mathieu would then build an international island city. The Emperor, however, was planning a 19th century version of Pearl Harbour and, for poor Albert's rather impractical scheme, that was that!

A year later along came the Englishman Mottray with the bright idea of laying a steel tube on the bed of the sea. Mark carefully the year—1803. We now know exactly how many years lay between the vision of Mottray and the emergence of techniques which could transform his pipe-dream(?) into reality.

Mottray's project was doomed politically, even before its practicality was examined, but a new germ, unknown to medicine, had been injected into the blood of engineers on both sides of the Channel. It lay dormant until 1833, when there appeared on the scene a personality who must surely have been the most colourful, and yet the most pathetic, in the history of 19th century engineering. Thomé de Gamond was then only 26 years old, but he was already qualified in civil engineering, mining, law, and medicine. He started off on the right foot, by insisting on the basic need for sound hydrographical and geological data. He laid the foundation for what was later to become a thorough knowledge of the rock formations below the bed of the Channel. In spite of all this, his first scheme, propounded in 1843, was so impractical as to be scarcely worth mentioning, except that it was, like Mottray's, a tube on the sea-bed, and that it was the first of a long series of Channel-crossing proposals which were to spring from this agile and fertile mind.

During the middle 1830's, de Gamond produced four bridge schemes and wound up the decade with yet another kind of plan —this time for embankments, leaving a central gap to be crossed by ferry. He remained apparently quiet during the 'forties, which he wisely spent gathering more information about the Channel bed, and it was 1852 before another scheme by Thomé twinkled—and was snuffed out. Having at last squeezed out of his system any notion of bridging the Channel, he went after still more geological information, even to the extent of doing his own skin diving. It was literally "skin diving," for he went to the bottom, several times, naked as he was born.

He chose 1856—a particularly opportune year for French/ British relations—to produce a detailed plan for the tunnel. For the second time the Varne Bank was to provide the foundations for an artificial island and a harbour. This structure was to be named Etoile de Varne—not very aptly, since stars are usually friendly to sailors, whereas de Gamond's Star of Varne would lie in the middle of the busiest shipping lanes in the world. To make matters worse, the ventilation shafts, which would have to be provided where the sloping approach tunnels met the horizontal main tunnel, would further shrink the navigational safety factor.

This was the first scheme to be considered at Government level. Enthusiasm flared up in France, and even in Britain something approaching tolerance was shyly exhibited; it seemed that something might happen. But Prime Minister Palmerston douched it with political cold water, which was promptly frozen solid by the attempt to assassinate Napoleon in 1858.

The next decade of 1860-1870 is notable in three ways. First, for a large number of wild-cat schemes; secondly, for the two most important proposals of the 19th century, which served to elevate the project out of the realms of science fiction; and thirdly for the formation of the first of the finance companies, so starting up a history of political and financial juggling which was to present an even more complicated chronicle than the technical history. One of the so-called wild-cat schemes was that of James Chalmers who published a booklet describing his "Channel Railway connecting England and France." It was remarkable for the pulpit quality of his English, and for his amusing and somewhat satiric descriptions of earlier schemes.

The year 1867 brought co-operation for de Gamond with William Low and Brunlees (two eminent British engineers experienced in underground work); they jointly devised a scheme for two parallel railway tunnels, and presented it to Napoleon III and the Grosvenor Committee. Its passage through the various stages of approval was halted by the Franco-Prussian War of 1870-71. This was not only a national tragedy, but also a personal one for de Gamond, because, by the time the dust of battle had settled sufficiently for the financiers to clear their throats once more, Sir John Hawkshaw had completed independent but extensive hydrological and geological investigations. He produced a scheme for a single-bore railway tunnel, which some members of the Grosvenor Committee rather liked. This liking was duly peddled around, with the result that de Gamond's team gradually lost face, and in 1874 Hawkshaw's scheme was adopted as the official project by the English Channel Tunnel Company.

For the next twelve months the story is a complex tale of financial and political wrangling and wangling. Eventually, however, the two Channel Tunnel companies, the English and the French, received permission to dig. By this time, a great deal more had been discovered about the geology of the area involved, and the conclusions drawn at that time, although based on investigational techniques which might be considered naïve by modern standards, gave a fairly clear picture of the various rock layers below the sea. It was plain to see, even then, that the route for a bored tunnel would have to be chosen very carefully. It would have to lie entirely within one stratum of rock, which had a number of clearly defined characteristics, which must persist, unchanged, throughout the length of the underwater crossing. It seemed that there was such a stratum, and all seemed to be set for the start of an exploratory tunnel. Thomé de Gamond's death in 1876 was a double tragedy, for it occurred before he could see this temporary defeat of the reactionaries.

EN AVANT!

The French got going in 1878. Whilst they were industriously going ahead with what was to become two kilometres of pilot tunnel at Sangatte, the English team leaned on their shovels with traditional phlegmatic calm. There was no money. During the delay Hawkshaw's scheme lost favour, and Low was once again "with it," this time with the backing of the brilliant and indefatigable Sir Edward Watkin.

This delay had some saving grace, for it enabled the British engineers to benefit from some previous French experience.* The time-honoured method of drill—fire—muck-out (see page 34...), even in chalk, was slow (although it was the quickest known up to that time) and dangerous to a degree not even then fully understood. The French had discovered that chalk was sensitive to the jolting impact of explosives. The shattering

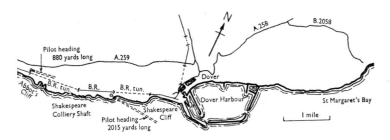

Fig. I   The English make a start, 1881

effects were transmitted readily through the rock, which would fracture and loosen far beyond the zone of the desired excavation. Exactly how far will probably never be known, but at some point under the Channel, the line of the tunnel could quite possibly approach nearly enough to a water-bearing layer of rock for blast-induced crevices to provide an inlet for water into the workings.   The effect would be sudden and disastrous and the decision not to blast in the chalk under the Channel was clearly wise.

So the British started their two pilot headings from shafts at Shakespeare Cliff and Abbots Cliff (Fig. 1) using Brunton's

---

*It was stated in good faith in Slater and Barnett's book that the Sangatte pilot heading was started by hand drilling and blasting.   This has since been denied by the best of authority and diligent research has produced no evidence that explosives were used at Sangatte.   It is possible that the error arose out of the difficulty of translating some archaic French in a paper published in 1882. There seems little doubt, however, that the French had had some adverse experience of blasting in chalk.

tunnelling machines. In the first of these headings, the Brunton machine was quickly replaced by the much more efficient Beaumont tunnelling machine. The French were quick to note the advantages of this machine, and soon had an improved version of it working in the Sangatte pilot heading (Fig. 2).

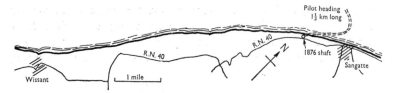

Fig. 2   The French make a start, 1882

CHAPTER TWO

Exodus

or how the idea was thrown out

SEDATIVE ADMINISTERED

THE TWO English headings reached for about 2,000 yards and 800 yards respectively before the work was stopped by the Board of Trade in response to growing public, political and military opposition. It seems incredible that most of the objections were based on the military vision of Frenchmen marching unimpeded to the conquest of Britain—a defeatist attitude of mind which was surely the worst insult the generals could offer to the rank and file of the British Army.

The tide of opposition rose to such a fury, it was a remarkable tribute to Sir Edward Watkin's tenacity of purpose that he was able to keep his engineers at work until July, 1882.

Meanwhile, the French went patiently on, hoping and waiting for perfidious Albion to sort herself out. The inevitable despair set in, and the final exasperation of the French can be gauged from their offer to build into the Channel Railway a loop which would carry the line out of the French cliffs on to a viaduct reaching out into the Channel, and back again into the cliffs, in such a manner that the Royal Navy could easily destroy it if and when British nervousness demanded the severance of the link.

The *coup de grâce* was administered by a Joint Select Committee appointed in 1883 "to examine and report." This Committee asked so many questions (5,396) of their witnesses, that even the French were shocked into immobility. In 1884, permission to continue the British exploratory work was finally withdrawn, and the tunnel was dead—like a phoenix!

MORPHEUS REIGNS

The only moves between then and the end of the 19th century were the reshuffling of companies and the changing of company names. There were some Parliamentary speeches, but they merely paraphrased all the old arguments, and were enlivened only by Gladstone's castigation of the chicken-hearted military. But Gladstone died in 1894, and Watkins in 1901, and the tragedy was as complete as the century. 20th century techniques of investigation have brought to light nothing which could show that the project abandoned in 1883 was not feasible and practicable, but in the 70 years since then, the price has gone up from a few millions to nearly £200 m. It should, in fairness, be pointed out that the rise in "real value" is very much less than this thirty-fold increase.

CHAPTER THREE

Reincarnation—ad infinitum

or Phoenix immortal

THE FIRT major move of the 20th century was made in the period 1904-7, when Low's plans were re-examined by Albert Sartiaux, who, with Sir Francis Fox of Simplon fame, brought the scheme up to date. Electric traction was now available, and this would permit faster acceleration, steeper gradients, and tighter curves and would also bring the ventilation problem within the bounds of reasonable cost.

The Sartiaux-Fox designs made use of every conceivable bit of previous experience and information. Their plan was soundly conceived and well presented, but this time the military's big guns were already loaded and the attack was immediate. The arguments raged wide and fantastic. At one stage, a French writer, Viernot, produced a book on military aspects. In one passage, he recounted how the French C.G.S. asked his Chief of Communications how he would get 150,000 troops through the tunnel from Wissant to Dover. He was told that it would take 15 days—provided "that everything was properly co-ordinated with the English authorities . . ." One could spend a whole hilarious chapter quoting the caustic and sometimes pitying comments with which Viernot demolished British military arguments.

But once again, the War Office won their bloodless victory by predicting defeat.

In 1913, the corpse was astir again, but hardly was the lid off the coffin than the 1914 war put it smartly back. It is difficult to resist the exercise of useless conjecture as to whether, if the tunnel had been in existence before 1914, the war would have positively confirmed or refuted the Army's long-standing dissidence.

After the war, in the enthusiasm to rebuild the world so as to be fit for heroes to live in, it was natural for the grandiose scheme to be revived. The proposals were still very much like the 1874 (Low) and 1914 (Sartiaux and Fox) schemes, but a new idea for disposing of the excavated rock seemed likely to be of great economic significance.

Once again, French enthusiasm was quenched by British Government opposition, and the excuse this time was $2\frac{1}{2}$ million unemployed. France, of course, had the same problem, but they offered to build the whole tunnel themselves, and since, in this way, the economic veto pronounced by Prime Minister Macdonald was made to look ridiculous, he had to fall back on the well tried delaying tactics of referring the problem to committee.

In 1923, the proposals were again exhumed, and there were murmurings of Parliamentary approval, but in July, 1924, the generals bared their teeth, and showed yet again that they could not be overruled.

Baldwin succeeded Macdonald in 1925, yet it was not until 1929 that, prodded by growing public opinion and a reiterated French willingness, Baldwin appointed a Royal Commission. After the most thorough investigation yet made, this Commission reported in 1930, and their famous Report, which is still obtainable from H.M. Stationery Office, is 90 pages of solid "gen." On the last page, they reach the conclusion "that the Channel Tunnel could be built and would be of economic value." The report was presented to the newly formed British Channel Tunnel Parliamentary Committee, which had an all-party membership, drawn from both Lords and Commons.

The Parliamentary arguments following this Report were diverse and devious. There is little point in giving any details of them, because they were much the same old arguments as before. The proposals, which were considered feasible by the Report, were quickly negatived and the best that the Committee could do was to try to maintain public interest in the Tunnel.

The war of 1939 prompted the inquiry as to whether the Channel Tunnel could be built quickly enough to be of use to the Allied war effort—surely an ironic enquiry to come from so largely a military body as the Supreme Allied War Council! A short sharp discussion on feasibility and construction time quickly closed, leaving only the irony as a reminder that it ever took place. The same thing happened again 2 years later, with even less hope and less success.

A decent interval of 2 years was allowed to elapse after World War II, but the rise of the new phoenix was not to be denied, and in 1947 began what might be called the modern history of the Channel Tunnel. Basdevant produced a refined proposal for a single large bore to carry both rail and road traffic. The threat (later realized) of enormous increases in private-car ownership and road transport generally made it difficult to dismiss his plan without very serious consideration. It did not, however, come up to scratch, in the British view, on the questions of ventilation and geology. It is odd that so brilliant an engineer should have insisted on a route for his tunnel which had long been known to be an invitation to disaster from a geological point of view.

The year 1947 marks, somewhat indefinitely, the beginning of what is very definitely a new and spreading confidence in modern developments of the method first proposed for the Channel Tunnel by Mottray in 1803. This method is now generally known as the "immersed tube" method. Perhaps "prefabricated subaqueous tunnel in trench," which is more descriptive, would be too much of a mouthful.

The second half of the century was heralded by a number of political and financial developments, which, although of considerable importance, have been reluctantly excluded from the scope of this book. It is, however, worth recording (merely for emphasis, since it is already well documented) that in 1953, on February 16th, Mr Harold Macmillan, who was then Minister of Defence, "admitted" that strategic considerations need no longer be considered an insurmountable barrier to progress.

Basdevant revived his proposal in 1958, this time refined in co-operation with three other French engineers*. It was hardly noticed by the public, perhaps because in the preceding year, 1957, a really positive move had been made towards sorting out the many problems which still existed, even after so many years and so many previous investigations.

*From this point onwards, so many eminent names have become involved in the Channel Tunnel project that it is deemed wisest not to mention any more.

The present Channel Tunnel Study Group was formed in July, 1957. It consists of four companies associated on an equal basis: The Channel Tunnel Company Limited, the Compagnie Financière de Suez, the Société Concessionnaire du Chemin de Fer Sous-Marin entre la France et l'Angleterre (the French Channel Tunnel company), with its associate, the International Road Federation (Paris Office), and Technical Studies, Inc., of New York. In the following 4 years this consortium was to spend more than half a million pounds on marine and geological surveys in the Channel, and on economic, traffic, revenue, and engineering studies.

The first phase of the group's studies was undertaken by four firms of Consulting Engineers, who reported to the group in December, 1959, on the "engineering feasibility and cost of the Channel Tunnel project." An abridgement of this report was made available to the public in March, 1960.

The investigation was very thorough—as far as it went. It confirmed everything that was already known. It confirmed a great deal that had been previously merely surmise. It found nothing to suggest that a Channel Tunnel was not technically feasible, but . . .

To enlarge further at this stage would be to encroach on the following chapters. It may be enough to say that, at the time of writing, yet another geological investigation is being conducted in the rocks beneath the Channel, in order to find out positively, not the feasibility, which is already accepted, but the best method of building whatever is to be built, exactly where it should be, and the snags which will arise when doing it.

PART TWO

A boring tale

which is not what it looks like but is in fact all about making a long hole under the sea-bed

CHAPTER FOUR

Ways and means

which is basic English for "preliminary considerations
of the fundamental techniques of tunnelling prior to
an appraisal of their applicability"

THREE MAJOR questions dominate any general discussion on the
Channel Tunnel. They are:
1. Can it be built?
2. Will it be built?
3. When will it be built?

They almost form a three-phase history of the 19th and 20th
centuries.

Question 1, as we have seen, was first posed in 1802 and, in
spite of the practical experience gained in the early 1880's, this
question was not positively answered until recently, when its
discouraging brevity has been attenuated into what is almost the
corollary question of "What would be the best way of doing it,
so as to encounter the least danger and difficulty?"

The second question too has teetered for a long time, and
has elicited many tentative yeas and nays, but has only recently
become more prominent than question 1. A bluntly positive
answer is still wanting, and will depend on the settling of a
number of ancillary questions—political, financial, legal, and
economic, now being hammered out.

On the third question, the crystal ball is still of milky hue, but
it seems likely that after a decision to build has become quite
positive, the "when" will not be delayed for many years.

Accepting the feasibility of such a project, this book will be
confined to attempting a simple explanation of those engineering
principles which have been slowly established during centuries
of tunnel engineering, and to showing how they can be harnessed
to the task of building the greatest tunnel of all.

Nowadays, it is probably true to say that engineers can build a tunnel anywhere they want to, but in no other field of civil engineering development has nature so closely guarded her secrets, or so grudgingly allowed her defences to be pierced.

The earliest reliable records of tunnelling date back more than 2,000 years. Roman engineers were quite undaunted by the problems of tunnelling through the hardest of rocks. In view of the limited tools and techniques at their disposal, and in the absence of any records of their failures, the Roman engineers of that time are to be much respected. Their skills, especially in tunnelling, were but scantily improved for the next 16 centuries, until, in fact, the invention of pneumatic drills enabled high explosives to provide a sudden great step forward in the rate at which rock could be excavated. The time and labour involved were reduced in proportion, and the economic results are obvious. The major problem of hard-rock tunnelling was under control.

In parenthesis, it should be mentioned here that, even in hard rock, it sometimes happens that the rock is so badly cracked and weathered that normal methods of drilling and blasting are too dangerous to use. The techniques employed in those conditions are arduous and expensive in both time and money. The danger of roof falls can never be entirely avoided. There is no point in discussing this problem here, because, if no Channel crossing route could be found which entirely avoided such conditions, there would be no chance at all of building a Channel Tunnel.

At the other end of the geological scale, development had to tread more cautiously. The problem when digging a tunnel through very soft ground, such as sand or soft clay, is not so much the difficulty of getting the ground to yield up its substance to the digger, as to prevent it yielding more than he wants to take away. Having made his hole, or more usually, even while making it, the tunneller must prevent the sides and roof from falling in. In early days, the miner proceeded cautiously and slowly, carefully shoring up the walls and roof with heavy timbering, until such time as he could make a more permanent lining of bricks and mortar. Sometimes he even had to fix boards across the working face, leaving only a small opening where he was actually plying his pick and shovel.

If the ground was wet (i.e. saturated with natural ground

water) the difficulties were multiplied. If the water could penetrate and move within tightly packed soil, how grateful it would be for a man-made cavity which it could so easily fill, drowning the invaders of its privacy.

These and other problems have been dealt with by using tunnelling shields and compressed air.

Between these extremes of dry hard rock and wet mud, nature provides a wide transitional range of "middling" ground, with infinite variety, for the perplexity of engineers who are trying to provide an underground passage. It should be remembered that, within each of the "extremes" of the ranges of hardness, there is also a wide variety, and there is no clear cut dividing line where drilling and blasting becomes impracticable, or where shield driving becomes impossible. But there is definitely a range of middling ground hardness, in which neither method is economic (when measured against the other means of providing transit from here to there). It was for this range that tunnelling machines were first developed late in the 19th century, and have more recently been developed to the high degree of efficiency which has made them the first choice for the task of boring under the Channel.

So we now have three fundamental tunnelling techniques, and according to which of the three (overlapping) ranges of hardness present their problems to the engineer, so does he have to choose one of three completely different ranges of method, plant, and labour skills. If his tunnel has to pass through two or more types of stratum, even perhaps within the same range of hardness, he starts having nightmares. And if these different types are far enough apart in the scale of hardness he gets no sleep at all. For clearly, if the line of the tunnel must, for some reason, pass from one to another of the three ranges of hardness, then all or most of the equipment must be withdrawn, and another set of plant, with the personnel skilled in its operation, must be installed at the working face.

This is the fundamental reason why one of the conditions to be satisfied—before the building of a Channel Tunnel can be considered feasible and economically possible—must be the finding of a route under the sea which will take the tunnel through only one kind of rock.

The first really obvious condition is that the route must be within a few miles of a line drawn from Dover to Calais, where the shore-to-shore distance is of the order of 20 miles. This narrowness persists for only a short distance to the south-west, before the Channel widens out rapidly, and the possibilities peter out beyond Folkestone on the English side and Cap Gris Nez on the French side. It would appear at first glance (Fig. 3)

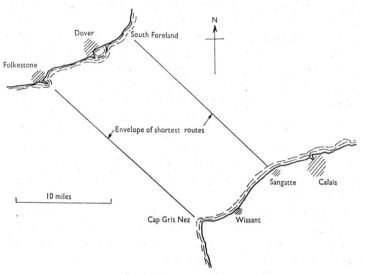

Fig. 3   The narrow gap

that the tunnel could cross the Kent shoreline almost anywhere between Folkestone and South Foreland. After all, if it is to be a bored tunnel, it must be at a safe depth before it leaves what the map shows as "dry land," and this, together with the high cliffs which stretch almost unbroken from Folkestone to St Margaret's Bay, means that there would have to be several miles of approach tunnel sloping up to the exit (the "portal") on the British side. Surely, one might ask, the route for this approach tunnel will be chosen so that the shore crossing could be made at the most convenient point to suit any alignment decided upon for the main tunnel? The conditions on the French side are somewhat similar, although in general a much shorter approach would be required.

So far, then, we seem to have established two imaginary parallel lines across the Channel, which are the north-eastern and south-western limits of an area through any part of which the tunnel could run. Within this area (not forgetting, of course, that we have a considerable choice of depth) it is possible to find routes which pass through each of the three types of ground for which the three different techniques of tunnelling could be used.

It is in this respect that the Channel Tunnel is an exception to the usual pattern of tunnelling requirements. Remember that its object is to provide a dry passage between England and France, and the locations of its portals and the necessary railway terminals depend only upon the availability of land on which to build them, and the need to link them with the main traffic routes of both countries. Any other tunnel, however, has to be located much more precisely, since its purpose is to provide communication between two points of much tighter geographical definition. So the route it must take usually gives the engineer little, if any, choice of the geological nature of the material he has to excavate.

Here, then, is the fundamental difference between the problem of the Channel Tunnel and the engineering approach to any other tunnel. For an ordinary tunnel, a thorough geological investigation must be made, along the proposed route. Then the method of tunnelling is chosen so as best to cope with the established ground conditions. For the Channel Tunnel, however, the possible variation of alignment permits the first step of considering all possible methods, then deciding on the combination of tunnelling method and ground conditions which would give the most economical results, and finally searching among the wide variety of rocks beneath the Channel for a route which would permit the chosen method to be used. It is for this reason that the Author has chosen to discuss tunnelling techniques before geology—a sequence which would not be countenanced in any other circumstances. So we will have a brief but closer look at the three techniques and see why two of them must be discarded and why even the third is limited to use along a particular line.

CHAPTER FIVE

The hard way

which is basic English "for the technique of tunnelling through dense strong homogeneous rock"

CYCLING

IN HARD rock, the tunnelling procedure is usually described laconically as "drill, fire, and muck-out." Each of these words hides a multitude of techniques and arts. There is almost infinite variation and only the briefest introduction to them is possible (or necessary) here. Before the repetitive cycle can begin, some preparatory work must be completed.

The first task, after assembling the necessary plant and labour force, is to establish a "working face," preferably a vertical surface. Since a tunnel usually enters sloping ground, this entails excavating a cutting, which gradually deepens until a point is reached where the cost of digging another length of cutting would equal the cost of boring the same length of tunnel. Here, a portal framework is built, together with any structure which is necessary to prevent the fall of material from farther up the slope into the working area (see Fig. 4). The criterion of equivalent cost may involve quite complex problems in the estimating and design departments, but it is likely that the work has now penetrated the overburden (the soft ground overlying the rock) and the rock itself is exposed to the miner.

In long tunnels, it may be necessary to have more than two working faces (one at each end). Clearly if four tunnelling teams can be working simultaneously instead of only two the tunnel will be driven in half the time. To do this a shaft can be dug part of the way along the line of the tunnel. When the shaft has reached the correct depth, tunnelling can start in each direction—by hand tools at first—until there is enough working space to mechanize the operation and to use explosives.

The basic principle of blasting is to loosen a volume of the virgin rock in such a way that, when it is removed ("mucked-out"), the line of the tunnel has advanced a distance (known as

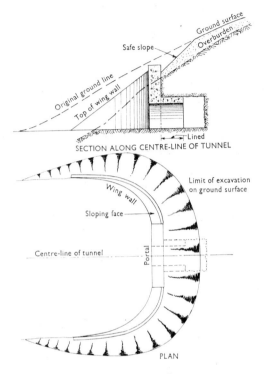

Fig. 4 Making a face

the "pull") in the correct direction, with, as nearly as possible, the correct cross-section.

Drilling

The first step in a cycle of operations which will be repeated as often as necessary—according to the length of the tunnel—is to drill holes into the working face. The arrangement of these holes is called the "drilling pattern," and it is carefully designed to have a number of interrelated characteristics. There are many variables involved, each one sensitive to changes in all the others. So, experience plays a great part in the final decisions on the drilling pattern to be adopted. And even this is frequently varied in the light of subsequent experiments, which can only then be related to the actual conditions of the rock which is to be excavated.

The following are some of the factors which affect or depend upon the drilling pattern.

1. The holes must be easy to drill. This seems perhaps too axiomatic to be worth mention, but it should be remembered that it may be necessary for other reasons to drill deep holes with machines held very close to the rough surface left by the previous blast. This may be difficult with the heavy, mechanically-held drifter type of drilling machinery, and even the lighter and more manoeuvrable type of hand-held drills are no featherweights, in spite of well-intentioned claims by plant manufacturers.

2. The periphery of the space left after the blast must conform as nearly as possible to the required cross-section. This is particularly important where a tunnel has to have a lining. For example, in Fig. 5, the captions given to all features in

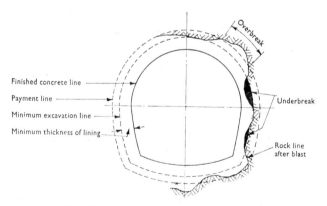

Fig. 5 Features of a blasted cross-section

the drawing are self-explanatory (except, perhaps, for "payment line"). The most important features costwise are the "underbreak" and "overbreak." In the first case, the blast leaves the virgin rock protruding into a space intended for lining, which may be of steel plate, cast-iron segments, pre-cast concrete segments, or cast-in-place (in-situ) concrete.* The blast has not done its job properly and the additional work of dressing down the "high spots," usually by hand, is disproportionately costly in time, labour and money. Overbreak, on the other hand, has to be filled in as part of the lining. If the lining is of in-situ concrete, then the additional volume of concrete required to fill in the overbreak gaps could, in a tunnel 20 miles or more in length, be a very large item in the cost of the tunnel. If cast-iron seg-ments, or any other kind of segments are used for the lining, the space behind them must still be filled by grout, and this is probably even more expensive than the additional concrete required for an ordinary concrete lining. The obvious futility of making an unwanted space and then spending money in order to fill it again, emphasizes further the need to find, as early as possible in the contract, the best drilling pattern. There are modern developments in blasting known as the "pre-splitting technique," which could very consider-ably reduce the extent of underbreak and overbreak. Its use has, so far, been limited, but experience is encouraging. It consists in drilling a large number of closely spaced, small-diameter holes along the line where it is required that the rock should break away from the virgin ground. These small holes are charged with small quantities of explosive, which, when detonated, merely cause a continuous split to run from hole to hole, without causing any major movement of the rock. This is followed by the major blast in larger holes, which brings the rock down ready for excavation, leaving a comparatively smooth surface. The technique is expensive and could only be economically viable where the rock is very hard and difficult, where wall smoothness after blasting is very important, and where there is no alternative route offering easier conditions.

3. Explosives are expensive and must be handled with highly trained expertise at all stages from the entry of raw materials

---

*Brick lining is rare nowadays, and is usually confined to sewer tunnels.

into the explosives factory to the time when, after the dust of the detonation in the tunnel has died down, the blasting engineer is positive that none of the charges remains unexploded and lurks in the muck pile waiting for the unwary. The type of rock—its hardness, grain structure, etc.—dictates the total quantity of explosive required for one round*. The diameter of the holes is determined by the standard sizes of the cylinders of prepacked explosives supplied by the chemical factories. So, the minimum number of holes required in the drilling pattern and hence their maximum spacing are exactly determined. But condition 2 (see p. 36) may require a different spacing and more holes. The explosive then has to be redistributed, putting less in each hole. This may result in too coarse a fragmentation, and further changes are required to ensure that the lumps of rock resulting from the blast are small enough to be handled by the "mucking-out" machines.

And so it goes on, compromise and experiment, guided by experience until the best combination of variables is found.

Firing

The firing of the charges is nowadays always electrical. It is important that the charges be fired in the correct order. Simultaneous firing gives unpredictable results (perhaps because it is never truly simultaneous) and has long been superseded by what is known as controlled-sequence firing. This was first made possible on a scientific basis by the introduction in 1939 of delay detonators which could ensure that, following a single operation of the exploder plunger, pre-determined groups of blast holes within the round would fire at one-second intervals. This interval was too long for tunnel blasting, because of the risk of interference between successive rings of charges. Half-second delay detonators were produced, but controlled sequence blasting was not really successful in tunnels until delays measured in thousandths of a second could be reliably achieved. (This is yet another factor which is related to the design of the drilling

---

*"Round" is the term applied to the set of holes drilled, filled with explosive, wired, and stemmed ready for blasting.

pattern). The order of firing affects the shape of the muck pile and this is, perhaps unexpectedly, important.

Mucking

Once again there is a whole chain of related circumstances which condition the Engineers choice of equipment to be used for "mucking out." The size of the tunnel cross-section will largely determine the size of trucks or wagons which can be used for carrying away the spoil. The bigger the better—for economy, but the size of the individual vehicles is not so important as the fact that one train of such vehicles, hauled by one loco-motive should be able to "load-out" (i.e. cart away) all the rock brought down by one blast. The vehicles range from tiny rail trucks holding half a cubic yard of broken rock in very small tunnels to large rail wagons holding more than twenty cubic yards. In some special cases, where a reasonably flat floor can be maintained, it is economical to use rubber-tired Diesel-engined trucks of road-haulage type.

The method of disposing of the spoil will decide if the trucks are to be side-dump, end-dump, or bottom-dump type (although this is not germane to the discussion here).

The trucks have to be filled from the muck pile, and here again plant has to be carefully chosen according to size of tunnel, type of disposal wagon, and the rate of working to be achieved, for example, in a small- to medium-size tunnel it is possible that the drilling pattern and firing sequence can be chosen so that as soon as the explosion fumes have been cleared away the drillers can start drilling the top holes for the next round whilst standing on top of the muck pile, at the same time as the loading machinery starts clearing from the bottom of the pile, see Fig. 6. There is no point in using expensive loading-out machinery of high capacity, if smaller, less expensive, and slower machines can still do the job without holding up any other operation.

The machines used for loading the muck train range from the small electrically or pneumatically driven overhead loader (Fig. 7a, p. 41) for small tunnels to very large excavators (Fig. 7b facing p. 48). There is also a wide range of self-charging conveyor-loaders (Fig. 7c), which spoon up the spoil in a series of jerks—

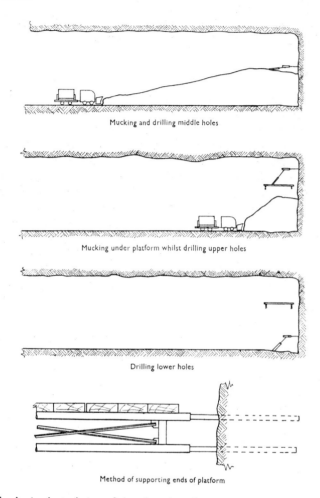

Mucking and drilling middle holes

Mucking under platform whilst drilling upper holes

Drilling lower holes

Method of supporting ends of platform

Fig. 6 A simple technique for saving time (by overlapping the drilling and mucking-out). See also Fig. 7c

quickly forward, slowly backward—on to a conveyor which loads up the trucks waiting behind.

These trucks must be brought up to the loader one by one, and problems of rail layout, switchgear, turntables and crossovers can be quite difficult. There are methods of loading a train of

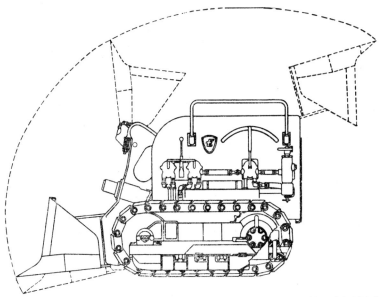

By courtesy of Eimco (Great Britain) Ltd

Fig. 7(a)   Rocker shovel

trucks without bringing each one in turn to the muck pile, but a discussion of these would take us wandering too far from our main theme.

LINING

There are few tunnels which do not require a lining of some sort.   Certainly, the most economical rock tunnel is the one driven through rock of uniform hardness, free from distortion by movement of the earth's crust, unweathered by exposure in former geological time, uncracked by seismic or volcanic influences, and above all, free from underground water.

The existence of any of these characteristics would create such difficulties in a 20-mile under-sea tunnel that the cost alone would prohibit the building of a Channel Tunnel.   But these unpleasant conditions are the same factors which dictate that the tunnel shall have a lining which is at least waterproof and may also have to withstand considerable pressures from rocks which can, at great depths, behave rather like a very stiff treacle.   On

41

the other hand, some rocks of volcanic origin can hide immense forces incurred by their original cooling down; these highly stressed rocks can burst violently, either immediately, or some time after, a hole is bored through them. Such violence is usually followed by a lengthy settling-down period and again, a lining affords protection.

It would seem then that a Channel Tunnel would be possible only in rock which, by the same token, would not require the tunnel to be lined. However, even the most kindly of rock is not entirely free from vice and it must be remembered that the tiny troubles which would be of small consequence in a short subterranean tunnel could become major problems 10 miles out under the sea. So all the Authorities concerned in the planning, commissioning, and operation of the Channel Tunnel have agreed that it must be lined, no matter what it passes through.

There are many ways of lining a rock tunnel, depending to some extent on the service the tunnel is to provide. For example, in some tunnels carrying high-pressure water for hydro-electric power stations, the lining may have to be designed to withstand internal water pressures higher than the external pressure exerted by the rock. In sewer tunnels the lining has to be proof against strong chemical corrosion and also prevent outward seepage which may contaminate local drinking-water supplies. And so on. Clearly problems like these are of no concern here and only the types of lining applicable to railway tunnels need be mentioned.

The traditional lining for railway tunnels has, for 200 years, been several layers of high-quality bricks. But the mind boggles at the astronomical number of bricks which would be required for a Channel Tunnel, and quite rightly, for the cost of bricks and bricklaying is now ridiculous. Until electric traction became common on the railways, concrete was not popular for tunnel lining, for it deteriorates rapidly under the chemical action of the sulphurous steamy conditions created by steam locomotives. But electric traction is now eliminating this problem, which is so serious that in the New Woodhead Tunnel, one of the first in Britain to be lined in concrete, steam locomotives are forbidden.

The brief description which follows of a method of installing concrete lining will quickly demonstrate, by contrast, the hopeless economics of using cast-iron bolted segments, where each unit has to be flanged for bolting, the joints have to be caulked with lead, and most likely the spaces between the flanges of each unit will have to be filled with concrete anyway. Add to this the need for filling up the overbreak outside the segments, and no more need be said of iron segments.

On the other hand there are three quite different methods of lining a tunnel with concrete which commend themselves to the Channel project, and of these only one is suitable for a "drill-and-blast" tunnel. This is the "in situ" lining in which the filling of the overbreak can be accomplished as part of the process of installing the main lining membrane.

It is well known that construction of "in situ" concrete requires first the erection of rigid shuttering (or formwork, as it is now more generally known). Steel or timber can be used, as circumstances and/or economics demand, but formwork must be so designed, fabricated and positioned that it fulfils all the following conditions:—

1. It must form a properly shaped vessel into which the freshly mixed concrete can be placed* and contained until it sets.
2. It must not "float" upwards under the buoyant influence of the lower layers of concrete.
3. It must withstand, without distortion, the pressure of the partly fluid concrete in much the same way as a water tank must be strong enough to withstand the water pressure at its deepest point. It must, furthermore, withstand the additional pressures imposed by partly fluid concrete which is being violently tamped (either by percussion or vibration).
5. It must permit the controlled escape of a small quantity of water from the concrete.†

---

*The word "pouring" is frequently used to denote the "placing" of concrete. It is a relic of the days when the concrete ingredients were mixed with so much water that the mixture was sloppy enough to pour. It has long been known that a much stiffer mix yields concrete which is better in every way. Modern concrete is, in fact, so stiff when it comes from the mixer that it has to be "persuaded" by mechanical tamping and vibration to take up the shape of the formwork which it is to fill.

†The minimum quantity of "gauging" water which can be used for mixing "workable" concrete is a little more than is necessary to complete the water/cement chemical reaction which causes concrete to harden. A little of this excess water can be allowed to remain in the concrete without harm, but in general as much as possible should be "persuaded out."

6. The formwork structure must be so sectionalized that it can be removed* from the set concrete. (In case the meaning of this is not clear the reader is reminded of the potter who moulded a beautiful slender-necked vase but could not remove his hand from the inside without destroying his masterpiece).

7. It must be possible to reassemble the formwork so that it can be used over and over again.

8. Finally and most important, as the word "formwork" implies, the shuttering must be so constructed that, when struck, it will leave behind a surface of concrete which is of the shape desired. In the case of a tunnel this is not complicated, and perhaps that is just as well, as we shall see.

Now all these conditions are common to practically every kind of construction in concrete. But for a tunnel there are some extra conditions:—

9. Unlike open-air building, where the shuttering can be struck and lifted by crane to its next position, the tunnel formwork has to be collapsed inwards, moved along inside the combined space it has helped to create, and re-erected ready for concreting the next length of lining.

10. Although the tunnel shutter must be strongly braced on the inside against the pressure of wet concrete, it must leave a clear passageway along the tunnel for access to the tunnel face.

11. Persuading the concrete to fill *all* the space between the outside face of the shutter and the rock is quite a problem. And checking that it has done so is another. Inspection trap doors have to be installed at frequent intervals in the shutter skin so that visual inspection can be made from inside the formwork.

12. In the case where the concrete of a section of lining requires longer to set than the time which can be allowed before the next section is started then there must of course be more than one formwork structure. In this case it must be possible for the first set of formwork when struck to be transported along inside the next formwork structure and

---

*The process of unsticking and removing the shuttering, so leaving the set concrete to support itself is known as "striking the forms."

then re-erected in advance of it, so allowing the next section of lining to be concreted before the shutter on the previous section is struck.

All these problems and many kindred ones have been solved by tunnelling engineers and countless monuments to their skill lie undisplayed beneath the ground. Figs. 8 (pp. 46-48) and Figs. 9 (facing p. 49) illustrate the manner of lining a tunnel with concrete, using a travelling leapfrogging shutter.

As mentioned on page 43, there are two other methods of lining a tunnel with concrete. Although different, they are closely allied, and both are less suitable for rock tunnels than the in-situ method; they will be explained later in a more suitable context.

It is in this respect of in-situ concrete lining that the hard-rock tunnel enjoys a great advantage over tunnels in softer ground. It is that if the rock is sound and free from water then the sides and roof of the tunnel, as blasted, can stand unsupported for any length of time that is convenient before the lining need be placed. This means that the two operations of excavation and lining can be kept far enough apart not to cause mutual interference. The rates at which the two operations can proceed are independent of each other and the planning of each is made correspondingly easier.

VENTILATION AND OTHER SERVICES

It is common to all tunnelling works, of course, that the atmosphere in which the miners work must be kept healthy. From this point of view alone, the quantity of air which has to be pumped into a tunnel is independent of the method of tunnelling. In the case of rock tunnelling, however, there is a periodic severe fouling of the atmosphere by exploding gases. These must be thoroughly cleared away before work can continue. It is a complex problem to pipe fresh air to the tunnel face, to pipe back to the open air the intermittent charges of foul gas, and at the same time to permit enough of the air supply to escape through the main tunnel to maintain a breathable atmosphere for what may be miles of infrequently used space. There is an expression—"as free as the air we breathe"—used to describe what does not have to be paid for. The "air we breathe" in tunnel workings is by no means free in this sense. Its provision requires expensive and complicated machinery outside the tunnel, properly housed, maintained, and supervised. Long

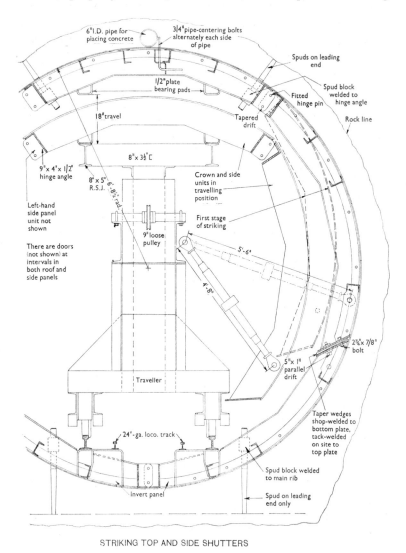

STRIKING TOP AND SIDE SHUTTERS

Fig. 8(*a*)   Leap-frog shuttering (see also Figs. 8(*b*) and 9)

pipe-lines and the necessity for ample standby equipment to allow for breakdowns put up the price of tunnel air until, in a very long tunnel, the air supply becomes one of the major items of the total cost.

The supply of high-pressure air for operating machinery becomes a minor problem in long tunnels, since compressors for this purpose can be installed in the tunnel itself. However, the release of air at high pressure into a dust-laden atmosphere can cause mist and reduction of visibility. This has to be allowed for as part of the "atmosphere maintenance" problem.

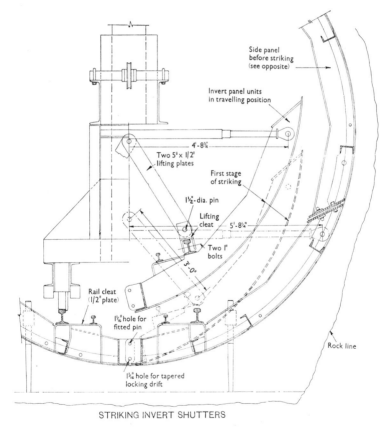

STRIKING INVERT SHUTTERS

By courtesy of Edmund Nuttall Sons & Co. (London) London, designers and users, and of Robert L. Priestley Ltd., manufacturers

Fig. 8(a) continued

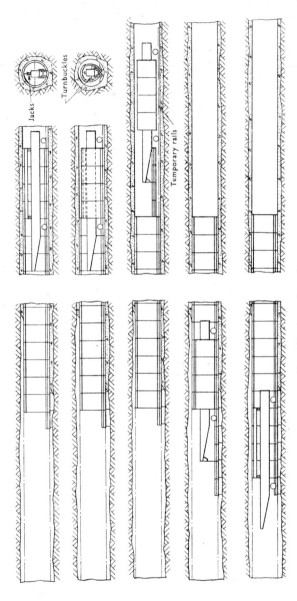

Fig. 8(b)   Leap-frog shuttering

Fig. 7(b)   The big boys at work

By courtesy of Distington Engineering Co. Ltd

Fig. 7(c)   Shaker and duckbill

By courtesy of Nuttall and Priestley (See Fig. 8(a))

Fig. 9(*a*) Bringing the partly folded invert shutter from its last position through a section of completed tunnel shutter towards the next length of the tunnel to be concreted

By courtesy of Nuttall and Preistley (See Fig. 8(a))

Fig. 9(*b*) The invert section of shutter, which was being brought forward in Fig. 9a, has been opened out into position. The partly collapsed roof-and-side shutter is now being brought through to join it

Other services, such as water supply, electricity supply, telephone lines, repair and maintenance facilities, medical care, etc. raise no special problems except that as the length of tunnel increases, the cost of the services rises exponentially. It should be remembered too that electrical current leakage must be assiduously avoided since it can cause premature and accidental detonation of explosive charges.

Compressed air for maintaining air pressure in the workings above atmospheric has not been mentioned here for a reason which will be made obvious later.

RECAPITULATION

There are many other problems for the rock tunnelling engineer, but this might be a suitable point to recapitulate and summarize what appears so far to be the make-up of a tunnelling plan.

The over-simplified description of rock tunnelling procedure —"drill-fire-muck-out"—can now be re-stated in a rather less curt list of essential operations:—

1. Assemble mechanical equipment and labour force.
2. Excavate the tunnel approach from ground level.
3. Establish the tunnel portal and the first underground working face.

Then the cycle of:—

4. Drill the first pattern of holes.
5. Remove drilling equipment from the face.
6. Pack the holes with explosive, wire up and stem.
7. Remove all equipment and men to a safe distance.
8. Fire.
9. Blow out the fumes.
10. Load the spoil from the muck pile into the muck train and carry it away.
11. Extend rail tracks (if used), lighting, power supply, air supply, etc. to the new face.
12. Drill the holes for the next round.

There are several interesting and important factors missing from this list but they will be mentioned later when appropriate. Its main purpose now is to bring attention to those items, numbered 4 to 11, which are repeated over and over again until the tunnel is complete. Although Items 10, 11, and 12 may overlap, even to the extent of starting and finishing simultaneously, the whole series—4 to 11—is called the "cycle." Every facet of the planning of a rock-tunnelling operation is aimed at achieving a "cycle" which can be repeated consistently and reliably.

Now the most efficient way of using skilled labour in tunnelling works is to observe the principle "each man to his trade." Add to this the fact that it is uneconomical for men to work shifts of less than 8 hours and inhuman to expect them to work shifts of more than 12 hours (both figures, of course, including travelling time to and from the face). It is obvious how easily these figures can be fitted into daily working of one, two, or three shifts. The result is that in rock-tunnelling works the most acceptable cycle time is 8, 12 or 24 hours.

This takes us back to a reconsideration of the choice of drilling and loading-out equipment. The most suitable tools are not necessarily those that do their job in the quickest time. It may be more economical to use slower equipment provided that it can do its job reliably and regularly within that portion of the cycle time which is allotted to its task. The machine which does a job and then has to stand idle waiting for a chance to do the next job is an anathema to a civil engineering contractor.

No universal set of rules exists for choosing drilling patterns, explosives, and plant. Each case must be dealt with in the light of experience, and, where this is inadequate, experiments must be made until the best answer is found.

And now the rate of advance becomes significant. The daily progress of the tunnel driving is of course the "pull" of each round multiplied by the number of cycles per day. The result of this calculation, when applied to those rocks, beneath the Channel which would require the drill-and-blast technique, is a rate of tunnel driving which is unlikely to exceed 400 feet per week. This assumes a uniform continuous stratum in which the tunnellers can peg away consistently, day and night (they wouldn't know the difference anyway), without the fear that they will meet underground water or that the rock walls will collapse about their ears as they go.

Much higher rates of driving have been achieved in much harder rocks but usually during short period of especially con- centrated effort. To maintain a rate of even 400 feet per week continuously for more than 20 miles would be heroic to say the least. We shall see later that this rate is rather less than can, in fact, be achieved, with more hope of consistent reliability, by another method of tunnelling in a different type of ground. At the same time it can be shown (a) that the drill-and-blast method of boring could not compete cost-wise and (b) that the lining (see pp. 41-45) of a blasted tunnel would also probably be more costly. The results of these and other more complex calculations in the estimating office show that the traditional hard-rock tunnelling methods simply could not be considered seriously for the Channel Tunnel. And so the process of elimination has begun!

CHAPTER SIX

The soft way

which is basic English for "the technique of tunnel driving with a shield for continuous ground support and possibly assisted by compressed air"

QUARTET

AT THE other end of the scale, what is rather loosely known as "soft ground" presents an entirely different set of problems to the tunneller. But first it should be explained that the range of soils now to be considered really consists of four overlapping types which used to be distinguished by graphic terms, only one of which was "soft ground." Taking these terms in descending order of the difficulty which they portray, the first is "running ground." The meaning is clear and the implication is that all surfaces of the tunnel must be continually supported, even the working face. Only a tiny area of the virgin ground may be uncovered at any one time so that the miner can control and dispose of the spoil which enters the working space through that opening—usually without waiting to be dug!

Slightly removed from this, the soil may be cohesive enough for a newly exposed vertical surface to retain its shape for a few seconds before the squeezing pressures behind cause it to bulge inwards. If at the same time the roof or any overhanging surface refuses to stay put—even momentarily—such soil is what used to be termed "soft."

A little further along the scale there is soil (and there are some types of rock) in which both roof and sides (not forgetting the floor, which in softer soils is just as troublesome as the rest of the surfaces) will stand unsupported for a short time. The name given to this was "firm ground," although too often was the terminology a snare and delusion.

To complete the quartet of what were once grouped together as "heavy ground" there is "self-supporting ground" which, if treated with respect, will stand without assistance for an indefinite and indefinable time.

A little more detail will be revealing, and may excuse the apparent looseness of the present day use of the single term "soft ground" to cover several types formerly so carefully distinguished.

Running ground.—This consists of gravel, sand, silt, or mud. These words are really only "grain-size" variants of what is known to the geologist as non-cohesive soils. Whether wet or dry*, they will "run," if a tunnel is bored through them. There was a saying frequently used by the occupants of shell holes during World War I—"If you know of a better 'ole go to it." Surely this must have been the heartcry of the first tunnellers in running ground.

But seriously, the difficulties of driving for any distance through this sort of nightmare are obvious, and since, beneath the Channel, there must be more than one "better 'ole," no more mention will be made here of "running ground."

Squeezing ground.—It does not require much imagination or tolerance to allow this term to include the second and third types mentioned above. In both cases, *some* support is required immediately, and in both cases, all-round lining (i.e. total support) must be installed soon. The soils which make "squeezing ground" comprise clay, soft earth, damp sand, and some of the softest rocks, such as cemented sands and crumbling chalk. All of these can be dealt with by "shield driving," which will be described later.

Self-supporting ground.—This includes hard-packed clay, sandstone, and cemented gravels, and was included in the early tunnellers' description of "heavy ground," because working in it required similar methods. Nowadays, however, more efficient ways of dealing with self-supporting ground have been perfected, and it is no longer in the same category of difficulty as "squeezing

---

*There are some exceptions to this. For example, damp angular-grained sands have a little cohesion; some sands and gravels may have become cemented by the chemicals dissolved in the ground water which has run through them; mud can be dry and caked, but this seldom happens underground.

ground." And so, for the purposes of discussion here, the field is reduced to "squeezing ground," and it is only this type which need be considered in a description of "soft ground" methods, insofar as it is related to the possibility of tunnelling under the Channel.

FOREPOLING—FATHER OF THE SHIELD

It is not so long ago that there was only one basic method of burrowing through soft ground. It had many minor variations, but there was a common denominator called "forepoling." This word seems at first sight to be self-explanatory, but in fact it is but a vague signpost to a complex operation in old-time mining. Reduced to its barest essentials, the forepoling (or "spiling") process is a cyclic operation, during the whole of which the tunnel roof, sides and floor are supported by a timber board lining, the boards themselves being strutted by square frames (called "sets") of heavy timbers. The working face which is to be cut away at the next "advance" stage is also supported by horizontally disposed boarding, which is held against the earth face by struts from either the last-built square set or from byots, which are heavy horizontal timbers spanning from side to side of the tunnel and firmly wedged in place. The first phase of the next cycle is to build what looks like a timber lining inside the existing boarding—(roof, sides and floor, or roof and sides, or roof only, depending on the quality of the ground). This inner lining is made of boards, all sharpened to a chisel edge pointing towards the working face. These are the "poling boards," and they slant outwards slightly, so that, when they are all driven (one by one) into the virgin ground, they will, in effect, form a continuation of the existing timber lining.

The face-lining boards can now be removed, or perhaps merely eased, one by one, and, as the ground behind each board is carefully removed, the board is "advanced" to its new position and strutted. In this way, little by little, with constant, painstaking and nerve-racking labour, the whole face is advanced to the end of the last-driven set of poling boards. A new supporting frame ("set") is erected to support these peripheral poling boards, converting them into the next length of lining, and so setting the scene for another advance cycle. There is, of course, a great deal more to it than described here. A much better description is given by Sandström*.

It is apparent that the progress of forepoling is so slow that it could never have been considered more than fleetingly for the Channel Tunnel. Why, then, mention it here? The first reason, perhaps, is a sentimental mourning for a lost art. Although spiling is still used in the odd length of bad ground within a longer run, other methods prevail in this age of mechanization, and the old-time sensitive tunneller, who can "hear the ground talking" or, perhaps, feel it moving, has had little opportunity or incentive to pass on his skills.

Secondly, and, of course, the real reason, is that modern developments in shield and shield-digger tunnelling (see p. 68) incorporate means of supporting the ground ahead of and behind the excavation face, which are unashamedly descended from forepoling.

THE SHIELD

Engineering history abounds with cases of the more primitive animals providing man with ideas for overcoming the strictures of his environment. The making of human history has been largely a consequence of man being able to leap far ahead of natural evolution by applying his inventiveness to developing these basic ideas. So it was with that small marine creature called *Teredo navalis*, or ship-worm, which treats undersea timbers in much the same fashion that the wood beetle destroys furniture in the homes of the unwary.

At a time when engineers had been scratching their heads for inspiration on a method of putting the first tunnel under the Thames from Wapping to Rotherhithe, and had pronounced it impracticable, Marc Brunel was observing a *teredo* boring into some oak in a shipyard. He noted particularly how this mollusc had developed two hard shells, which encircled its body and formed a completely circumferential protection, fitting neatly inside the diameter of the creature's "tunnel." The sort of protection that Brunel required was of a rather different

*G. E. Sandström. "The History of Tunnelling." Barrie & Rockliffe, 1963, pp. 110-113.

nature, but the idea was sprung. From it, he developed a structure which is now looked upon as the first-ever tunnelling shield.

A detailed description of Brunel's shield has no place here, except to say that it gave all-round integrated support to the freshly-dug tunnel, until the lining could be installed. The face was also fully supported, whilst giving the necessary access for a number of miners to cut away at limited areas of the vertical surface. The ground was stiff blue clay and the whole contraption was shoved forward by screwjacks, which kept the skin surrounding the shield cutting into the clay, always slightly ahead of the miners. Here can be recognized the "forepoling" action. Although reliable historians freely attribute Brunel's inspiration to the ship-worm, this author feels that Brunel himself might have encouraged the belief—in modest rejection of the credit for a brilliant development of the art of forepoling.

Be that as it may, the Brunel shield was not an unqualified success, and it was twenty-five years before the next attempt to burrow beneath London's river brought to light the forerunner of all subsequent tunnelling shields. Barlow and his pupil, Greathead, drilled the Tower Subway from Tower Hill to Tooley Street. It was a small job by today's standards, but was a turning point in tunnel history, for it was completed without mishap of any kind, and, although it has been closed to the public for many years, it is memorialized in every tunnelling shield put into service during the past 100 years.*

By now the reader will be getting impatient for the reasons why the tunnelling shield merits such a long introduction. A description of its operation is surely due now.

First it should be clearly understood that the word "shield" means what it says. It is not in itself an excavating implement but is basically a movable frame which supports the working face and the ground immediately behind it: it gives protection, as its name concisely implies, to tunnellers as they excavate and line the tunnel. Fig. 10(a) on p. 58 is a simplified diagram of the essential parts of a tunnelling shield.

A glance at the photographs in Figs. 11(a) and (b) (facing p. 64) will help to make the drawing clear. It should be remembered

---

*It is coincidental, but a source of satisfaction, that the proposed publication date for this book will mark the centenary of Barlow's Shield Patent.

however that the photographs are of two actual shields, whereas the drawing is not of any particular shield but is a concoction designed to show the principles of construction and operation.

First, there is outer envelope of steel plating—the "skin"—which has a diameter slightly larger than the outside diameter of the lining which is to be installed.

Fitted into the front end of this skin is a very strong framework which is usually built up from a number of steel castings. The forward edge is sharpened to form a circular knife or "cutting edge." The cutting edge is often shaped so that its upper half is a foot or so in advance of its lower half, as shown in Figs. 10 and 11(a), both of which depict this type of hooded shield. The hood is particularly useful when the soil at the working face is very prone to collapse or when the porous nature of the ground would permit the easy escape of air from the workings. Such an escape would be especially dangerous when compressed air is being used to prevent the flooding of a tunnel in very wet ground. The operation of the hood is illustrated in Fig. 12 on p. 60, which explains the method of "clay pocketing."

The "working chamber" or space in which the miners actually work when digging is within the "cutting edge" frame and immediately behind it is a diaphragm. The "aperture" in the diaphragm gives access to the working chamber but can be closed in an emergency to form a water-tight seal between the face and the tunnel. Where the ground is so bad that the face has to be continuously supported by boards ("poling boards"), small hydraulic rams (Fig. 11(a)) are provided in front of the diaphragm to hold these boards in place. Behind the diaphragm is another strong frame which supports the skin in its true shape against the severest outside pressure and also provides housing for the main hydraulic rams. These rams push the shield forward, embedding the cutting edge into the ground ahead of the working face. When the rams are fully extended they still do not quite reach the rear end of the "skin" of the shield. It is inside this last few inches of skin that the latest lining ring was erected. (The lining ring shown in Fig. 10(a) is noted as being of cast iron, but it could equally well be of any other material which would form a continuous water-tight lining, resistant to external pressure).

Figs. 10(a) and 11(b) show that the rams have steel pads fitted

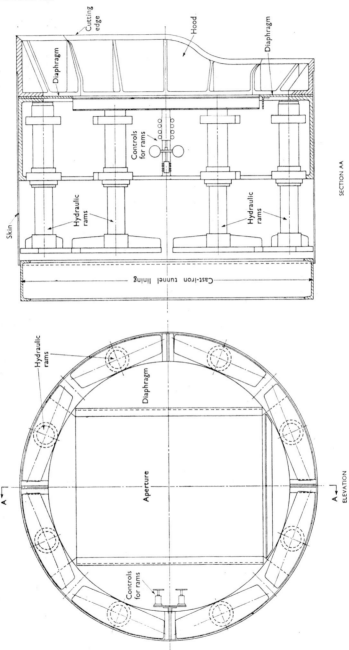

Fig. 10(a)   The principal features of a tunnelling shield

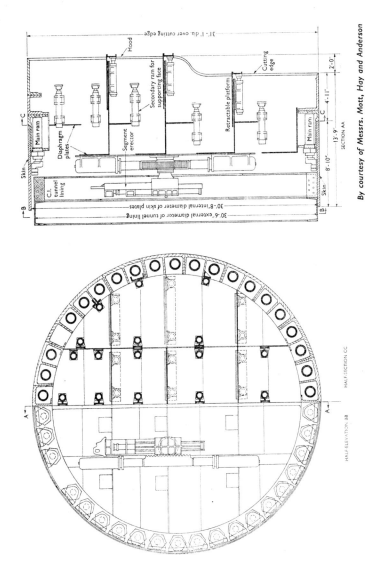

By courtesy of Messrs. Mott, Hay and Anderson

Fig. 10(b)   Shield used in Dartford Tunnel

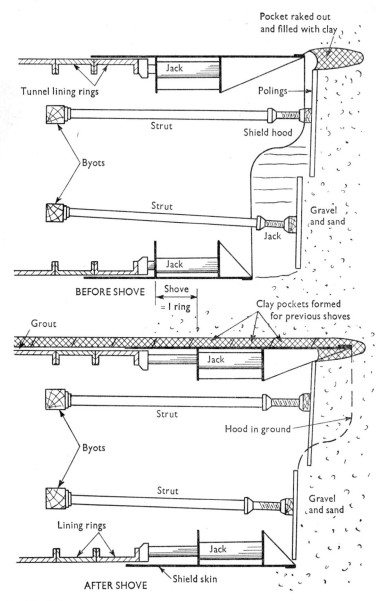

Fig. 12 "Clay pocketing," using a hooded shield with compressed air, in sand and gravel

at their rear ends so that when they are pressing against the front flange of the lining ring they exert an even pressure all round the ring. It is this pressure against the installed lining which pushes the shield forward into the virgin ground. A different method of providing a footing for the "shove" is illustrated in Fig. 10(*b*), which shows the details of an actual shield used for a large tunnel under the Thames. Here the shove required so many jacks and they were therefore so closely spaced that the spreader plates were not required. The ram pressures were transferred through lugs welded inside the skin. The rams are individually controlled by a set of valves mounted on a control console, and it is the skill of the operator in manipulating these valves which ensures that the shield moves straight forward, or up or down, or to left or right, as the excavation proceeds.

KEEPING THE FACE DRY

In the diagram there is a slight space between the lining ring and the ram heads. This is a particular phase in the cycle of operations. The rams, formerly pressing against the lining, have pushed the shield forward as far as possible; they are in an early stage of being withdrawn into their cylinders and when the withdrawal is complete there will be sufficient space inside the skin and between the present lining ring and the ram heads to install the next ring of lining. The rams will then be brought to bear on this new ring and the forward shove will start again. Following this process through it will be seen that the naked ground is never exposed and the seal, all the way from the diaphragm backwards into the completed tunnel, remains unbroken. (It will be seen too why the method of continuous in-situ lining used for tunnels cannot be used behind a shield).

Compressed air can be given only a fleeting mention if this book is to be contained to one volume. The reason for using compressed air is simple; it keeps out the water. It is well known that the air pressure in a diver's suit must be increased as he goes deeper into the water. In order that his suit should not collapse, the air pressure must always be matched to the depth of the water above him. This depth is known as the "head," and the air pressure which keeps the suit inflated at any depth can be measured in "feet head of water" as well as in "lb. per square, inch." Now if a tunnel is being driven in wet ground, the pressure of the water trying to get into the tunnel (whether pouring in or merely seeping in) is the pressure caused by the "head" of water over the tunnel, that is to say, the height of the water surface above the workings. If the air pressure in the tunnel is increased to match this "head" then there is a balance of forces, and the water is kept out.

The equipment involved in maintaining this air pressure is extensive and expensive; the mechanical and human problems are complex. So much so that if no route can be found for the Channel Tunnel which does not require the extensive use of compressed air, then it might be a fair assumption that the conditions down below are too hazardous for a project of this magnitude to be undertaken at all.

There are, however, modern methods which eliminate the need for compressed air where it would formerly have been essential. These are the techniques of soil stabilization by which the ground ahead of the working face can be injected with solidifying chemicals, or cement grout, or gelling ("thixotropic"*) clays. The shield can then be safely pushed forward through the stabilized ground.

KEEPING THE TUNNEL DRY

Having successfully built our water-tight tube behind us as we progress, we still have to remember that the thickness of the shield skin which separated the lining ring from the earth surface will leave a space *outside* the tunnel, which must be filled. For this purpose, plugged holes are put at suitable intervals in the lining components. Each plug is removed in turn and a pipe connected for grouting—a process in which a fluid cement or cement/sand mixture is pumped into the space outside the tunnel. This is done as soon as possible so as to give the ground little chance to settle and distort, so setting-up uncalculable stresses in the tunnel lining.

We have seen how, in the rock tunnel, the excavation can go on far ahead of the lining work—if any lining is necessary. We

---

*A "thixotropic" material retains some degree of stiffness or "non-fluidity" so long as it is undisturbed, but immediately becomes fluid when stirred. "Thixotropy" is the property claimed for some modern "non-drip' do-it-yourself household paints.

have seen too how the lining in a "soft-ground" tunnel must be installed immediately as the shield takes every step forward. The methods of lining are equally diverse. In-situ concreting of long lengths cannot follow a shield and the lining must be installed in short lengths equal to the travel of the shield rams. These short lengths are the "lining rings" mentioned earlier, and each consists of a number of preformed segments, made outside the tunnel and transported to the workings for assembly and installation. Apart from bricks—a form of precast lining which we have already scoffed at for the Channel Tunnel—the earliest form of prefabricated lining was of cast-iron segments. Each segment is part of a circular arch with flanges at both sides and ends so that bolting through the end flanges forms the segments into a ring and bolting through the side flanges forms the rings into a continuous tube. The outside of this tube is usually grouted, as we have already seen, but no possible precaution against leakage is overlooked and all the joints between segments and rings are caulked. There is a choice of materials for caulking but probably the most popular is lead-wool, which is hammered mechanically into the grooves which are formed half in each flange so that when the flanges are brought together the grooves mate up into a single channel to accept the lead.

Although cast iron still provides the most satisfactory form of precast lining in soft ground, it is very expensive and a great deal of extra work is required after the segments are put in place. This method is being largely supplanted by precast concrete segments, which are cheaper although generally cast into a very similar shape—each segment can be imagined as a double-ended trough bent into an arch. The trough permits bolts to be fitted through the side and end flanges, and can then be filled with in-situ concrete if a smooth interior is required in the tunnel.

Steel plating can also be used for lining, but this is mainly in hydro-power tunnels, which carry high-pressure water and so require the lining material to have high tensile strength.

A modern alternative to the flanged and bolted concrete precast segment for tunnel lining is the concrete "voussoir." It is well known how an arch is given great strength by giving each block forming the arch a slight taper, so that when all the blocks are in place the temporary supports ("centering") can be removed and the multiple wedging action makes the arch self-supporting. The tunnel lining ring built of voussoirs is merely an extension of the arch into a full circle.

A number of tunnels have been built recently using concrete voussoir linings, and since they are not all bolted together, a complete ring of the blocks has to be supported temporarily until the keystone is set. Machinery, consisting of hydraulically operated curved arms, cradling a number of voussoir blocks on each side of the tunnel, is installed at the rear of the shield, together with a crane which loads the blocks on to the arms.

Our simple shield, now shouldering its additional duties is beginning to look like a space-age monster.

This form of precast block lining offers the opportunity for taking much of the tunnellers' work out of the tunnel itself into large-scale factory production line. This is particularly attractive for the Channel Tunnel—whichever way it may be driven.

There is yet a further development of the voussoir block principle which is also bound to be a strong contender for the honour of providing shelter to the under-Channel traveller. In this method, known as the "Don-Seg" system, the voussoirs are not only tapered in a direction towards the centre-line of the

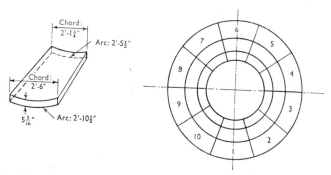

Fig. 13 "Don-Seg" precast segment and a perspective view along the tunnel to show the order of placing successive rings of segments (The dimensions are those specified for a particular tunnel and are shown here merely to demonstrate the "taper")

tunnel but also along their lengths as shown in Fig. 13. To install a ring of Don-Seg precast concrete segments the ring is built up with the taper alternately fore and aft. The segments

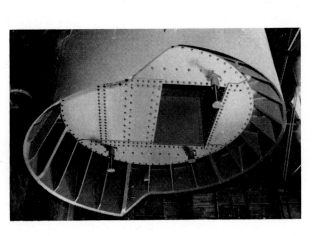

Figs. 11(a), (b)   Front and back of a 13-ft.-1-in.-dia. shield

By courtesy of Mr. S. C. Sargent

Fig. 15   Robbins Mechanical Mole

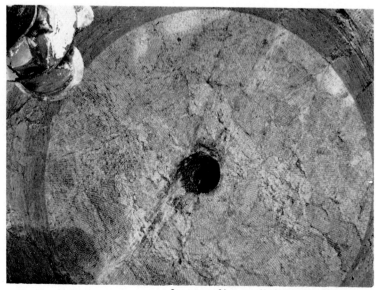

By courtesy of Lawrence Machine and Manufacturing Inc

Fig. 17   The working face in a hard rock tunnel being drilled by an Alkirk Tunneler
(See Fig. 18)

which have their wider ends towards the previously installed lining ring, are pushed up tight to that ring. The remaining segments then fit snugly, but not tightly, into the alternate spaces so that their wide ends stand about 4 inches proud of their companion segments. The proud-standing segments are then rammed fully home until all bear evenly against the previous ring. This wedging action all round the ring expands the diameter of the ring slightly so that it now completely fills the diameter of the tunnel as driven, and no external grouting is necessary if the dimensions of the segments have been sufficiently accurately designed.

Such then, is the equipment and technique for driving a tunnel through "squeezing ground." There will be many questions which have had to be left unanswered if this discussion is ever to come to an end. There are infinite variations aimed at safety and efficiency, both during and after construction.

RECAPITULATION

In Chapter 2 we saw how the tunneller would deal with hard rock, and realized how much more complicated it is than just chiselling a big hole. So much so that when we added together all the costly processes it became clear that if we could avoid hard rock under the Channel it would pay to do so. Now what of the other extreme?

The answer here is not so quickly reached. The risk of blasting causing rock failure far beyond the range of instrumentation and setting the scene for unexpected and disastrous roof falls is replaced by the more persistent danger of water, mud, and running sand. But these can be discovered by safe exploration ahead of the tunnelling operation and the necessary measures can be taken in time to deal with the hazards.

In brief, there is no doubt that if the only route under the Channel required shield driving then it could be done. But in the same way that a motorist, having found one suitable route on his road map, will look for a better one, so does the engineer show only lukewarm enthusiasm for the first method which seems feasible for a large project.

So having now explored the shield driving method and agreed

its feasibility, we must also agree on what advantages we can hope to find in any method yet to be discussed.

In the first place, shield driving in squeezing ground is slow, and this becomes important when the distance is 20-odd miles. Secondly, the driving and lining must proceed at the same pace, so that if the driving becomes difficult and suffers delays while forward grouting consolidates the occasional patch of running ground, machinery and labour will be standing idle and the cost per foot of drivage rises rapidly.

So we are led to an examination of past experience where shields have been used for driving through "self-supporting ground" (see page 53) with rapid and uniform progress. But we are now getting into that range of ground hardness which, for the purpose of this discussion, has been called "middling ground." The reader is therefore to be kept in suspense regarding the rejection or acceptance of shield tunnelling for the Channel with the promise that the next two chapters will complete the picture for him.

CHAPTER SEVEN

The middling way

*which is basic English for " the technique of tunnelling by
rotary machines through rock which is not hard enough
to require loosening by explosives nor soft enough to
require continuous support "*

IT WAS tempting to call this chapter simply "Tunnelling Machines"
but that might have implanted the idea that the mechanical
equipments used in hard- and soft-ground tunnelling are not
machines. Of course, drilling jumbos, rock conveyors, and
concrete placers are all machines. So are shields, with their
complex systems of rams and controls, lining erectors, and so on.
Nevertheless, modern tunnellers have come to use the term
"tunneling machine" for a particular kind of machine which has
been developed to eliminate hand digging at the tunnel face.

A natural line of thought would run as follows. For a hundred
years or more, all "soft-ground" tunnelling has been done with
the protection of a shield, which was originally devised to give
protection to the miners in their back-breaking task of digging
away the face material and loading it into vehicles for "mucking
out." Just before the turn of the century a start was made on
the tubular tunnels for London's Underground. The stiff clay
through which they were being driven was so uniform in consistency and yet so laborious to dig manually that it cried aloud
for a mechanical digger. The conditions were ideal for the
development of a rotary excavator consisting of a series of chisel-
like cutters mounted on arms radiating from a central shaft.
As the shaft turned, the chisels ("picks") gouged circular grooves
in the clay face, removing some of it in long strips as if peeling
an orange. Between the grooves (known as "kerfs") were left
circular ridges (or "lands") of clay which were now so narrow
that they were easily scraped off by the spade-like buckets,

which were mounted so as to follow the picks and scooped the excavated clay on to a conveyor belt for mucking out.

All the rotating gear was mounted centrally in an ordinary tunnelling shield, and so improved the "rate of advance" that the shield could be rammed forward at three times its former speed.

Stronger and more wear-resistant steel alloys became available and in a later development, the picks and buckets were replaced by curved spades mounted on a rotating drum which is driven by gears mounted between its circumference and the inside of the shield. This machine, in its most modern form, known as the "Drum Digger," is being used now for driving the new Victoria Line addition to London's Tube system.

We are still, of course, talking about tunnelling through "squeezing ground" but as the material gets harder and comes into the self-supporting range, then we approach "middling ground" which requires no shield. So it is natural to take the shield away and leave only the rotary excavator, which is what we now call the "tunnelling machine" although the "cheese-paring" tools may have to be replaced by something more substantial.

It would seem then, that the tunnelling machine was a natural development of the shield. Now for the bombshell! Two of the earliest tunnelling machines were developed especially for use in the Channel Tunnel which was so gaily started in 1878. The first of these was, by today's standards, a rather Heath Robinson affair, but its successor, the Beaumont tunnelling machine was similar in conception to the first rotary excavator described above—but without the shield. Indeed its appearance shows that it was designed for cutting harder stuff than clay and the protection of a shield was clearly not contemplated.

For the next half-century or so the idea of tunnelling by machine lay dormant in spite of the rapid development of mechanical miners in the coal industry. But in the past two decades great strides have been made.

Here a little digression might be useful, for the design of tunnelling machines is constantly being aimed at harder and harder rocks. How hard is rock? Indeed, what is rock? This is not as stupid a question as it appears, for tunnellers speak of "ground." How hard does the ground have to be before it is called rock? Perhaps the simplest way to define it would be to say that a piece of rock requires to be fractured in order to change its shape, whereas a lump of ground which does not qualify as rock can be pressed or kneaded out of shape. (This is not strictly accurate: in some circumstances rock deep down can behave in plastic fashion; on the other hand some cemented sands can behave like rock. However, the distinction is good enough for our present discussion.)

Now we are in the range of rocks, how hard is soft rock, how hard is hard rock?

Geologists use a scale of numbers from 1 to 10 as a guide to the hardness of minerals (using the word in its correct sense, not as an alternative to "animals" and "vegetables"). Rocks however are usually composed of different minerals cemented or fused together, so these numbers really should not be used for describing rock hardness. Nevertheless they do provide a rough and ready means of comparing the hardness of different types of rock, so long as we remember that a rock of average hardness 5 will probably contain a number of minerals of a wide range of hardnesses. And if there is one component mineral which is very hard it will of course be that mineral which plays havoc with any tools we use for boring through that rock. With these reservations one can say that hardness Nos. 1 and 2 refer to talc and chalk, 3 and 4 to slate, limestone, and sandstone; in the middle of the range are granite (4.2), schist (5), and basalt (7); whilst numbers at the top are really out of the range of rocks and refer to the harder gems, carborundum (9), and diamond (10).

It will be clear by now that tunnelling with a machine which can chew its way relentlessly and steadily through the rock beneath the Channel will be quicker, cheaper, and in every way a better proposition than drilling and blasting.

It is important therefore to see how far modern engineering has forced upwards the dividing line between "middling ground" and "hard rock," that is to say, how far in the rock-hardness range can tunnelling machines now replace the more tedious drilling and blasting.

We have seen how a series of rotating picks cuts concentric grooves in hard clay and so mutilates the face that any material which does not fall away is easily scraped off the face by the following buckets. As the ground gets harder, however, the picks have to be made narrower so that they will penetrate. (More picks at closer spacing is no answer because there is a limit to the power which can be applied for both pushing the machine forward and rotating the cutting head).

Between the concentric grooves ("kerfs") the remaining ridges of material (now to be called "rock") are virtually undisturbed. So the picks are followed by intermediately spaced rollers, each made of hardened steel, with a sharp edge (see Fig. 14), so bringing very high pressure on to the middle

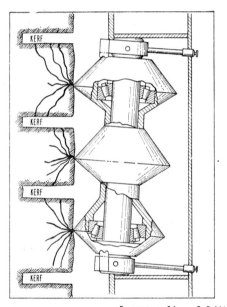

By courtesy of James S. Robbins & Associates, Inc

Fig. 14 "Mole molars" (hardened steel sharp-edged rollers mounted on a rotating head)

of the ridge or "land." The effect is seen in the diagram, and the shattered rock falls away or can easily be scraped away.

This type of machine was first developed in America and a large number of them are in service all over the world. The machine illustrated in Fig. 15 is being assembled. (The pick-type kerf-ring cutters have not been used on this type of machine since 1960.) It was used for driving large river-diversion tunnels during the building of the Oahe Dam in America; and some hydro-power tunnels in Tasmania have been driven by a smaller version of the same machine. The largest so far built is driving five 32-ft.-diameter tunnels through sandstone and limestone for the Mangla Dam power tunnels in Pakistan. For the mechanically minded, Fig. 16 describes the essential parts of a "mechanical mole," which, it is claimed, can bore through rock of a hardness which would correspond to No. 4 in the mineral hardness scale.

The diagram shows that this machine is fitted with a type of shield. It is not the sort of shield described in the previous chapter, but it provides protection for the workmen installing the ring-beam sections. These ring beams provide, in the first place, the purchase for the rams which are forcing the cutter head against the rockface and also provide anchorage for the gear which pulls the machine back from the face when required. Such retraction may be necessary for several reasons. The cutters and rollers need frequent replacement; or the machine may encounter a water-bearing fault, or a pervious water-filled stratum. In the latter case, immediate measures have to be taken to prevent flooding of the tunnel, and one of the limitations of machine tunnelling is immediately very apparent.

The "mechanical mole" in the form described can be fitted with different cutters according to the hardness of the rock. Each type of rock to be bored requires a unique combination of cutter configuration, thrust, and cutter-head torque for optimum boring performance, and each such combination is efficient over only a small range of hardness. Clearly then the machine is seen to its best advantage if the route followed contains only one kind of rock, for changing the cutters is a time-consuming and therefore costly business. We shall hear more of this later, but in the meantime, rock hardness of more than 4 in the mineral-hardness scale creates another problem, for then the pick-type cutters give up the ghost.

Omitting the picks releases a lot of power which can now be used to give a harder shove to a larger number of rollers, which

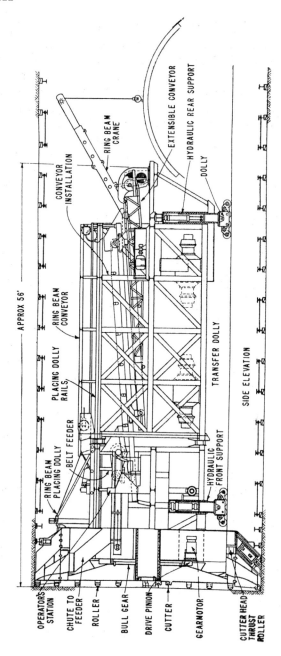

OPERATORS STATION
CHUTE TO FEEDER
ROLLER
BULL GEAR
DRIVE PINION
CUTTER
GEARMOTOR
CUTTER HEAD THRUST ROLLER

RING BEAM PLACING DOLLY
BELT FEEDER
PLACING DOLLY RAILS
RING BEAM CONVEYOR
CONVEYOR INSTALLATION
RING BEAM CRANE

APPROX 56'

HYDRAULIC FRONT SUPPORT
TRANSFER DOLLY
SIDE ELEVATION

EXTENSIBLE CONVEYOR
HYDRAULIC REAR SUPPORT
DOLLY

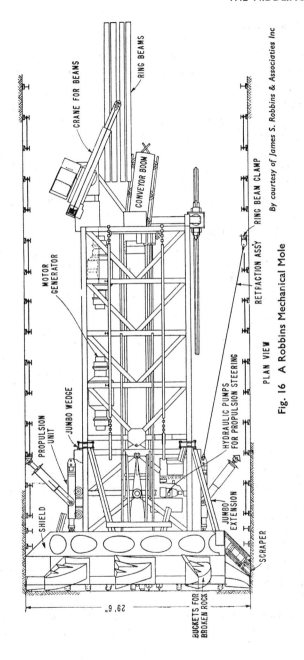

RING BEAMS

CRANE FOR BEAMS

CONVEYOR BOOM

MOTOR
GENERATOR

JUMBO WEDGE

PROPULSION
UNIT

SHIELD

RING BEAM CLAMP

RETRACTION ASS'Y

HYDRAULIC PUMPS
FOR PROPULSION STEERING

JUMBO
EXTENSION

SCRAPER

BUCKETS FOR
BROKEN ROCK

29' 6"

By courtesy of James S. Robbins & Associaties Inc

PLAN VIEW

Fig. 16 A Robbins Mechanical Mole

now have to shatter the rock face simply by concentrating very high pressures at more points on the rock face.

The latest development in this type of machinery departs from the principle of sharp-edged hardened-steel roller wheels, for these will not cope with the rocks which for a hundred years or more have been amenable only to drilling and blasting. Fig. 18 (facing p. 160) shows a machine which has recently been put to work in America, driving through schist. (Schist is something like slate but harder, and in this case contains feldspar and garnet, which has a hardness of 7 in the mineral scale). The rollers (see Fig. 18, inset) are fitted with inserts of sintered carbide (which is nearly as hard as diamond and much less likely to splinter). The inserts are arranged in such a way that they exert a continuous chipping-cutting action on the rock face.

This machine has a revolutionary feature, which Fig. 18 shows but does not explain. This is a mechanism which looks like a long nose in front of the array of rollers. Although first invented for use in coal mining in Alaska more than 10 years ago, it is new to rock-tunnelling machines. The idea is this: in previous tunnelling machines the thrust which had to be applied to the cutters was obtained by pushing backwards against the sides of the tunnel already dug, or against ring beams (Fig. 16) which had to be firmly anchored in the rock. The force which could be exerted was therefore dependent upon the strength of the ring-beam fastenings and upon the firmness of the rock, which, it must be remembered, is no longer in its natural state of high compression and has probably been weakened by release of stress. The new idea is to drill a hole, of only a few inches diameter, ahead of the main boring machine. This is done by the triple cutter on the front end of the nose. Then a collar is slid along the nose as far forward as it will go and expanded so that it grips evenly all round the hole, temporarily restoring the rock to its natural state of high compression and forming an almost unbreakable grip in which the main machine can then pull itself forward. In the machine, illustrated which bores a 12-ft.-diameter tunnel, the forward pull can thrust the cutters against the tunnel face with a force of about 350 tons, with self-centering action which greatly assists the steering of the machine.

Now what is the point of developing these machines to cut

harder and harder rocks? The main reason is that in any one type of rock a tunnelling machine will advance farther in a day than the most efficient system of drilling and blasting—so long as the rock is sound and continuous. With this proviso, the very high initial cost of such machines is more than offset by the reduced labour costs which come from shorter contract periods —and there are many other factors which make them cheaper overall for long tunnels. Not least of these is the fact that the smooth bore eliminates overbreak (see Fig. 17, facing page 00), and all the extra concrete lining which overbreak entails.

The continuous rotary tunneller has yet one more attraction. The ease with which a powder can be transported by flowing water stimulated the new idea for mucking out mentioned on p. 24. A hole drilled upwards from the tunnel workings into the sea-bed would ensure a plentiful supply of water! A pulverizer and mixer behind the tunneller could then convert the excavated material into slurry for pumping into the sea through a second hole. The advantages of keeping the completed part of the tunnel free of mucking-out trains are obvious but the economics have yet to be proven.

So, although we have already killed the idea of drilling and blasting for the Channel Tunnel, the tunnelling machine has buried it deeper than ever the tunnel will be.

But how do these machines fare in competition with shield driving? Clearly, the softer the ground the more likely it is to require the protection of a shield and all the ancillary techniques which go with shield tunnelling. On the other hand, as the ground gets harder from the "soft" range into the "middling" range, the more difficult it will become to shove the shield forward, and at the same time the more obvious are the advantages of a tunnelling machine. There must be an optimum type of ground in which the pure shield becomes uneconomical—and we have already buried the drill-and-blast idea.

So all we want now is to find a route under the Channel which runs entirely through the type of ground in which the tunnelling machine can show its paces to the best advantage. If we can prove that such a route exists, then we can banish the idea of shield driving to the same limbo where drilling-and-blasting now rests. But proving it requires another chapter or so.

CHAPTER EIGHT

Friends and enemies in the underworld

which is basic English for "a consideration of the geological conditions which are favourable or adverse to tunnelling progress

THE GEOLOGIST-ENGINEER FRIENDSHIP

TUNNELLING IS the most obvious of many engineering activities to be dependent upon a thorough knowledge of the earth's crust. Geology is the science which gathers and classifies this knowledge, using a standardized vocabulary, into an organized fund of information. From this constantly expanding storehouse of facts practitioners of many different disciplines, as well as engineers, can extract the data which are pertinent to the immediate problems, translate if necessary the geologist's terminology into their own jargon, and so make practical use of a pure science.

Geology is a vast and comprehensive science, and in spite of the fact that it deals very largely with what cannot be easily seen, it can make extraordinarily accurate and detailed predictions under a large area of the earth's surface by combining the visual evidence of changes in the ground surface with that of a few carefully located boreholes. How this is done is not relevant here; it is sufficient to know that the boffins *can* do it. But a brief outline of some of the queer things that have happened and can happen deep down in the ground, will help to confirm the wisdom of those decisions we have already made; and will help us to make up our minds in cases where we are still sitting on the fence. Before getting down to rock-hard facts however we must clear up one or two apparent anomalies.

No modern engineer would begin to think about making a tunnel without first extracting from every possible source of information all the facts which geological science can make available to him. Yet tunnelling was an established and successful practice a thousand years before geology became an organized science. This is really not surprising, for medieval tunnels were rarely long and there is much evidence on the surface of the ground from which the intelligent man can draw conclusions as to the possible configuration of the rock layers below the ground in the close vicinity. There were probably many more failures and disasters than have been recorded but a sufficient number of early tunnels remain to generate a sincere respect for those early engineers whose judgement was not aided by the precision of modern rock technology and measuring instruments.

Nevertheless there is reason to believe that the enormous increase in the volume of tunnelling works in the early nineteenth century was not wholly the result of the industrial revolution and its demand for a rejuvenated system of transport routes, water supply, drainage systems, and so on. Without the rapid strides made in the conversion of geological investigation from what was largely intelligent guesswork to a textbook science it is likely that many tortuous routes and long detours would never have been blessed by the short cuts which tunnels provide.

It is true too that, for some nineteenth and twentieth century tunnels, neither geographical nor exploratory techniques could provide enough information to prevent failures and disasters. It is this aspect that will be uppermost in our minds if and when men are working 300 ft. or more beneath the waves between Dover and Calais, and it is fortunate that the earth's crust can nowadays be explored by machines which will drill hundreds of feet downwards, even from the bottom of the sea, and bring to the surface cylinders ("cores") of soil or rock from all levels. This is the most valuable of all the kinds of evidence the geologist and engineer require.

There is one more preliminary hurdle to get over. This is a fundamental difference in the terminology used by geologists and engineers. To the geologist, everything forming the earth's crust is "rock," even if it has been weathered or ground down to sand or clay. He includes coal, which is vegetable in origin, and those rocks which are largely composed of the calcified remains of marine flora and fauna.

The engineer, on the other hand, thinks of rocks only as hard or compacted formations, but when they have been changed by nature into easily deformable material he calls the results "soils." We have so far avoided confusion by free use of the word "ground" and it is unlikely that any real ambiguity will arise in what follows. After all, we have already decided that if the right sort of "rock" layer can be found under the Channel, we need not worry about the soils.

It will help to understand what we are looking for if we know a little of the behaviour of different kinds of rock. This behaviour, as it is related to tunnelling, depends to some extent on how the rocks were formed in the first place and what has happened to them since.

ROCK TYPES

Before getting down to very detailed and scientific classification, rocks can be divided into three main types: igneous, sedimentary, and metamorphic. Frightening words perhaps, but, like most scientific terms, carefully chosen to avoid ambiguity.

The constituent materials of all rocks were originally in a molten state. The "igneous" group of rocks comprises those which are still in approximately the same condition to which they cooled and crystallized from molten material during the earth's long geological history. The word "igneous" should not be misunderstood, for these rocks do not result from the action of fire; the action is more correctly described as "freezing" or solidification from the liquid state. It was the association of all the crystalline rocks with the lavas extruded from volcanos which led to the accepted usage and persuaded compilers of dictionaries to include "of volcanic origin" as one of the meanings of "igneous."

During the process of geological time, such of the first-formed igneous rocks as became exposed at the ground surface became "weathered" and broken down, wholly or in part, into their constituent mineral crystals, many of which suffered both chemical and physical changes in the process. As has continually happened since, and happens today, the weathered materials were transported by rivers and other agencies to the seas of the period— seas that also attacked the edges of the land, again as modern seas do. Larger pieces of rock were rolled into pebbles, later to form beds of conglomerate. The remaining material was graded by water-action and laid down on the sea floor as beds of sand, silt, and mud.

These were subsequently consolidated to a greater or less degree into sandstones, silt-stones, and clays, either by pressure from materials laid down on them, or by some form of cementation.

It has occurred many times in the geological history of the earth that strata so formed on a sea-bed have been raised to become land areas, again to go through a weathering process and transportation of weathered debris by rivers to the sea. Some materials have been reconstituted several times. During these episodes, calcareous matter in the rocks has been dissolved in water to reach the sea in solution. Much of this has been incorporated in shells of marine animal life, and in some forms of plant life—notably highly specialized lime-secreting algae. In favourable circumstances great thicknesses of calcareous matter from dead organisms, and in some instances from chemical precipitation, have been deposited on the sea-bed, later to become limestones. Certain sandstones and clays and kindred rocks have been accumulated under desert conditions, partly on land, partly in temporary lakes.

All these last are "sedimentary rocks" and the term is unequivocable. Most sedimentary rocks are porous to a greater or less degree and many are highly permeable, notably sandy beds and some forms of limestone, composed of rounded grains superficially resembling fish roe. Other sediments, however, like clays, some of the chalks*, and close-textured limestone, are in themselves but little permeable.

The third main type is the metamorphic rocks. The degree of metamorphism that rocks undergo depends partly on the temperature or pressure applied to them and partly on the composition of the rock before it was altered. At one extreme, enormous heat and pressure have caused the rocks to recrystallize into

---

*All chalks are types of limestone. Most of them are permeable. In a few places the chalk contains a proportion of clay, and as the clay content increases so the chalk becomes less permeable. A full range of chalks, from very porous to almost completely impermeable exists beneath the Channel (see pp. 107-8).

forms quite different from those of the original; at the other end, constituents are rearranged within the rock but with little chemical alteration. For example, a pure limestone that has been melted recrystallizes into a pure white marble, and pure quartz sand or sandstone yields a white "quartzite." In neither case is there any change in actual chemical composition. Clays and silts under appropriate conditions react by undergoing a rearrangement of their particles so that the longer axes of all the particles lie parallel; there is also some degree of chemical change. It is in this way that slates are formed; their fissile character is a direct result partly of the orientation of the particles and partly of recrystallization.

A further stage in the metamorphism of clays and silts and of some other rocks produces "phyllites," which split easily into leaves. Yet a stage further and the original rocks become transformed into "schists", while an impure sandstone or other coarse-grained sediment becomes a "gneiss" which is a rock somewhat comparable with granite but with a laminated structure. Slate, phyllite, schist, and gneiss are all easily recognizable progressive stages of the same process.

THE ANTICS OF ROCK FORMATIONS

Igneous rocks occur in masses of various shapes and sizes; they may exist as great bosses whose lateral extent and depth are measured in thousands of feet; or they may exist as sheet-like masses known as sills and dikes, with a thickness ranging from a few inches to many feet and extending for distances of from a few hundred yards to many miles (these sheet-like masses were formed from molten material that had been injected along planes of weakness in existing strata); or the igneous rocks may be sheets of lava extruded over the local contemporary ground surface, although in many instances these are now buried by later deposits. Sedimentary strata are a direct contrast to this; by the very nature of their mode of formation they are stratified. Some strata are continuous over many miles and occur in thicknesses of hundreds of feet with only minor variation in the character of the rocks. It is more general to think of sedimentary rocks as groups of strata of different types alternating with each other; each group can extend over hundreds of miles and may be several thousands of feet thick, although within these groups individual beds of special kinds of rock may be thin and in places may fade out altogether.

Joints and Bedding Planes

All rocks contract in volume as they become consolidated. In all the harder rocks, both igneous and sedimentary, the stresses resulting from this contraction have led to the production of cracks; some of these are known as "joints" and others as "bedding planes" according to the cause of the cracks. Joints and bedding planes separate each rock mass into blocks. Igneous rock masses shrink during the process of cooling and the joints thereby developed normally divide them either into the more or less cubical units which occur in most types of granite, such as those easily seen in Cornwall, or into the hexagonal pillars so obvious at the Giant's Causeway in Northern Ireland and also on the West Coast of Scotland and in the Rhine Valley. The square and the hexagon are the only two geometrical shapes that fit into a compact pattern without the presence of other geometrical shapes. The hexagon form is characteristic of igneous rocks that have cooled from the upper surface downwards, and it is often seen in cracks produced in dried mud after the evaporation of water from puddles and ponds. Cubical masses are more consistent with a regular cooling and so they usually occur deeper where the escape of heat to the surrounding masses of rock has been more strictly controlled.

Sedimentary strata have become consolidated in the course of time, largely as a result of pressure from later strata deposited on top of them. The pressure produced an expulsion of some of the contained water and also possibly a rearrangement of constituent particles; the latter would cause a reduction in porosity. In the case of hard rocks such as sandstones and limestones, the decrease in volume was accompanied by the formation of cracks. Sedimentary strata were mostly built up by periodic accretions of new material, with a break in time between each addition. These breaks are potential or actual planes of weakness and a set of contraction cracks frequently developed along these

F

strata. These contraction cracks are called "bedding planes." Joints occur more or less at right angles to the bedding planes and to each other. These joints and bedding planes are of course open to the percolation of water and where this has happened many joints and bedding planes in hard sedimentary strata, particularly in limestones, have gradually become widened by the dissolving away of lime or other soluble matter. Extreme examples of widened joints are the caves of Cheddar Gorge and Ingleton in Britain, and there are mammoth caves in the limestone regions of the South of France. On the whole, sedimentary strata are more jointed than are igneous rock masses. A system of bedding planes and joints is shown diagrammatically in Fig. 19.

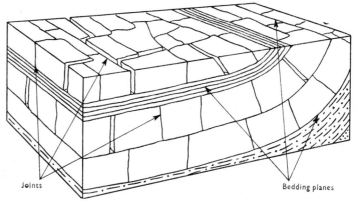

Joints

Bedding planes

Fig. 19   Diagram of typical system of bedding planes

Bending the Rock Layers

The great majority of sedimentary strata that now constitute land areas were originally laid down on a sea-bed. And, rather surprisingly, some of the highest mountain ranges in the world consist of what have been shown to be marine sediments. It follows therefore that there must have been some very violent movements in the earth's crust to cause these great changes in elevation and of course these changes are clearly accompanied by the many bends and folds which we know exist in geological strata.

Now once the set of strata has been folded and bent in this way it is only a matter of time before the now corrugated surface of the earth suffers further types of change. One of these is the effect of the variation in elevation causing differential static pressures deep down and this in turn leads to a slow but sure redistribution of the rock masses lying beneath. The second effect which occurs with time is the eroding away of the high spots, the ridges, and the hump crowns, so exposing the layers beneath and forming a series of what are called outcrops. After a rock outcrop has become exposed in this way it can then be covered by superficial sheets of gravel, sand, clay, and other materials that have accumulated during the immediate geological past. Such deposits are called "drifts"; they are generally thin and unconsolidated and are of little consequence in tunnelling operations of the subterranean nature. However when we start tunnelling beneath water then the drift may become important, because if the bed of the river or sea under which we are tunnelling has ever had a river channel cut into it then it is likely that this river channel has been filled with drift; this is not shown by normal exploration methods of the bed and the fact that they exist may prove to be of vital importance. Indeed perhaps one should say of deadly importance.

When the wrinkling of the rock layers becomes more than a mere undulation other unfortunate happenings take place. For example the stresses in the rock layers can become so high that all the layers break and we now have what is called a fault. There are several kinds of fault and two of these are clearly shown in Fig. 20. This diagram also demonstrates the meanings of several

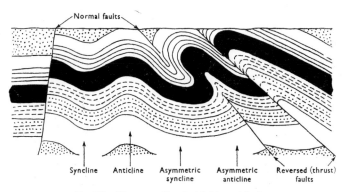

Fig. 20   Diagram of typical folds and faults

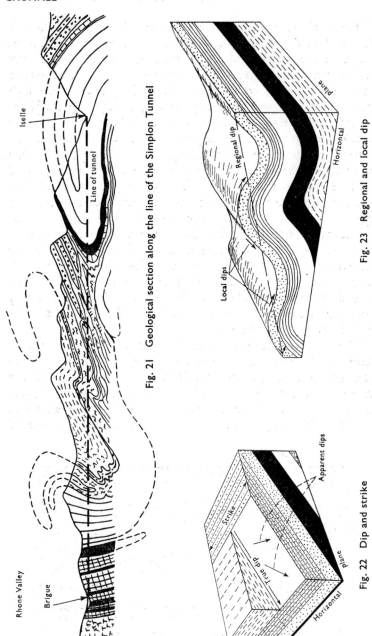

Fig. 21 Geological section along the line of the Simplon Tunnel

Fig. 23 Regional and local dip

Fig. 22 Dip and strike

other terms used in geology and gives a hint of what can be described as a tunnel engineer's nightmare. This nightmare is emphasized if we look at Fig. 21, which shows the salient features of the geology of the rocks through which the Simplon Tunnel was drilled. It is hardly necessary to say that if we could find nothing better than this under the Channel then the Channel Tunnel is hopeless from the outset.

Dip and Strike

One of the requirements of tunnelling geology is an ability to envisage blocks of strata from the view point of solid geometry. In some of these blocks surfaces of the various strata normally slope in one direction or another, whilst an imaginary line at right angles to the maximum angle of slope lies horizontally (see Fig. 22). The angle of slope is its "dip" and the direction of the horizontal line is the "strike."

In strata that are simply tilted, both dip and strike are relatively constant over wide distances, but in folded beds, such as in Fig. 23, variations from both the regional dip and the regional strike are numerous.

The plans of the joint systems, the frequency of bedding planes, the direction and degree of dip, and the existence of synclines and anticlines are all geological features important to the tunneller working in rocks. They exercise control over the natural stability of tunnel walls and affect the amount of over-break (see pp. 37-7). Some of the ways in which these features can present problems and dangers to the tunnelling engineer are illustrated in Figs. 24, 25, 26 and 27.

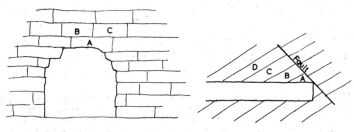

Fig. 24 Impending roof fall   Fig. 25 Impending roof fall

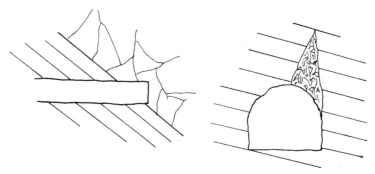

Fig. 26 Another dangerous situation   Fig. 27 Yet another

BUGS AND ANTIBODIES

Every one of the irregularities in rock formations is at least a nuisance and at worst a deadly menace to the tunnelling engineer. Wherever there is bedding plane or joint, fault or fissure, that is where nature has her strongest defences against the intrusion of puny man.   For it is at these places that rock falls and eruptions are most likely, and it is here too that underground water is a constant threat to the miner.

If the threatening water is merely that which is entrained in and percolating through the pervious rock layers which lie around, and immediately above, the line of the tunnel, then the flow of water into the tunnel workings is rarely of disastrous proportion*. It can usually be dealt with fairly easily, especially if it was known to exist.

But if we are under the sea, the water danger is in quite a different category.   It could be, of course, that a water leakage into a submarine tunnel turns out to be no more dangerous than in a subterranean tunnel.   This would be so if it were known that there is an unbroken impervious stratum between the water-bearing layer and the sea-bed.   But even here, there is a danger that the loss of water from a water-filled stratum of rock can so

---

*If the entrained water is under high pressure, its flow into the tunnel, although small in quantity, can be explosive in violence and result in extensive rock falls.   For this reason, many engineers do not accept the different evaluation made here of the risks involved in subterranean and subaqueous tunnelling in water-bearing ground.

alter the density and the consistency of that rock, that the support it gives to the "dry" layer above it is weakened and that dry layer might then be breached by the enormous water pressure above it. The result would be sudden and disastrous. This combination of circumstances is rare and unlikely, but the possibility exists.

Far more likely and equally dangerous is the condition where there is direct communication for water from the sea, *via* a fault or fissure into the pervious stratum. In such a case, nature can conduct her defence (which now becomes an attack) with unlimited reserves of enormous power.

Before a Channel Tunnel can be seriously attempted there must be absolute certainty either that none of these dangers exist, or that where they do exist, their locations are exactly known *before* they are encountered.

So much for the more important bugs which can infest our communication artery. What of the antibodies? What can the engineer look forward to as a help rather than a hindrance?

Prime amongst them are, of course, the procedures the tunneller himself can control. These are the techniques of drilling exploratory small-diameter horizontal boreholes far ahead of the tunnel base, and the grouting and other consolidation procedures which were mentioned on p. 62. But there are also some material advantages which make the prospects more hopeful.

There are three points of particular interest in this respect. The first might be described as a prayer waiting for an answer; the second as a predictable freak of nature; and the third as a prayer answered.

The Supplication.—The burden of this prayer can easily be guessed. It is that the rock formations beneath the Channel contain at least one layer which is:

1. Continuous and uniform in physical character (so that the same driving equipment can be used throughout).
2. Free from joints, bedding planes, faults, and fissures.
3. Dry and impervious.
4. Firm enough to eliminate the need for a shield.
5. Soft enough to eliminate the need for drilling and blasting.

6. Thick enough to contain the tunnel cross-section with a bit to spare above and below the tunnel.

7. Sufficiently free of undulations that the tunnel can be driven through it without anywhere exceeding the maximum permissible gradient.

It is the answer to this prayer which has been sought in every investigation which has been made into the feasibility of a Channel Tunnel, from the earliest efforts of de Gamond up to the drilling operations which are being conducted during 1965.

The freak of rock pressure.—This is a little more difficult to explain. First we must confine the discussion to ground which is "self-supporting." If the tunnel is not far below ground level, the most important pressure which has to be contained is that due to the weight of the overburden above the tunnel.

This weight acts vertically downwards and is normally quite easy to support by using an arch form for the tunnel roof. The strength of the arch in supporting vertical loads needs no explanation for it is very obvious in the bridges, doorways, and other curved structures which have used the arch form of support from time immemorial.

In this type of tunnel there is little or no lateral pressure on the sides, which can therefore be vertical, and the floor can also look after itself. The tunnel cross-section can then be the shape

Fig. 28 Tunnel in rock without side-thrust or up-thrust

Fig. 29 Horseshoe tunnel in rock subject to side pressure but no up-thrust

Fig. 30 Horseshoe tunnel in rock subject to both side pressure and up-thrust

shown in Fig. 28, and this shape is common in railway tunnels driven through hard firm rock.

If the rock is not so hard, or if it is water-bearing, there may be a sideways pressure on the tunnel walls, which is countered by introducing a minor arching effect on the side walls. And the tunnel becomes horseshoe shaped as in Fig. 29.

As the rock gets softer still, or as the depth of the tunnel increases, the pressure re-distributes itself and some uplift appears below the tunnel floor. So an "invert" (i.e. an inverted arch) is incorporated in the tunnel floor (see Fig. 30).

And now this re-distribution of the pressure becomes very important; at very great depths, the pressure in the rock behaves like that in a liquid and the pressure at any point is the same in all directions. This is the effect described in what is known as Heim's Theory of rock pressure. The shape of the very deep tunnel must be capable of withstanding pressure which is approximately equal in all directions, so the surface of the tunnel must face in all directions at once. This means of course that it must be circular. And a circular tunnel lining is, after all, an endless arch. That is to say, it offers the maximum possible resistance to pressure in every direction at once.

A Prayer answered.—This is the combined result of a number of factors of which we are now well aware. First, the tunnel under the Channel will be so deep that Heim's Theory (or what is left of it after some modern pundits have added their provisos and modifications) must be taken into account. It follows that the Channel Tunnel will be circular in form. Secondly, we already know that we are searching the Channel bed for a type of rock which lends itself to "machine driving." And thirdly, driving a tunnel by rotary digger clearly requires the tunnel to be circular (unless one can use one of the modern "continuous mining machines" devised by the National Coal Board for digging coal-mine headings). How neatly these three factors combine together to light up the Stygian gloom which always attends tunnelling among uncharted rocks.

We now have a single guiding star to steer by—a machine-driven circular tunnel through a uniform continuous homogeneous layer of not-too-hard rocks, and our only remaining major problem is to find out if such a layer exists.

CHAPTER NINE

The channel-bed layer cake

which is a tastier title than "the geological configurations which dictate the optimum route for the Tunnel"

WHAT DO WE REALLY KNOW ?

IT IS possible to say in the same breath that a great deal is known about the rock layers beneath the Channel and that very little is known about the rock layers beneath the Channel. An obvious paradox, perhaps, but each statement is true, according to one's point of view.

Remembering that no one has yet actually seen what lies more than a few feet below the sea-bed, it is truly remarkable how much information has been deduced from explorations below ground at and behind the two coastlines. Maps and cross-sections have been drawn and the technical arguments put forward by the investigators to justify their extrapolations are highly convincing.

On the other hand, as in all civil engineering, the facts which are not known are the most important if a tunnel is to be built. The risks which attend delving into the unknown are always an engineer's nightmare. Fortunately, the risk to human life can nowadays be considered negligible—the days are gone when such a low value was placed on miners' lives that the extent of precautionary measures was limited by their cost. The technical risk of being unable to complete a job, once started, because of unforeseen difficulties is also largely eliminated by the techniques which are now available. But there remains the financial risk of finding that the contingency allowance in a contract price is far exceeded by the cost of overcoming unpredicted technical difficulties. In a project the size of the Channel Tunnel this could spell disaster to any hope of repaying the cost of the work, unless we can become a great deal more sure than we are now that no geological dragon lurks in the hidden depths waiting to ingest the adventurers.

GETTING THE FACTS

How do we build up a knowledge of rock structure we have never seen?

This is a three-dimensional question, the answer to which has been obtained piecemeal over a very long period of time by many investigators. The most positive information has been obtained by making holes in what is virtually a single dimension —boreholes. Data of this unidimensional character were linked together by two-dimensional observations—out-crop areas. And the result is a three-dimensional picture. It is in this order that we shall build up our 3-D view of the Channel geology, for a chronological account of the findings would mean a great deal of dull repetition.

Turning first to the single dimension of a vertical line, our investigation is aimed at finding out the type and thickness of rock immediately beneath our feet, the type and thickness of rock immediately below that, and so on, through as many layers as necessary and to whatever depth the information is required. Until recent years, such an investigation was possible only when starting on dry land.

There are three* basic methods of getting visual evidence. The first consists in digging a pit, in which at least one wall is vertical and approximately smooth. This method is only useful for very shallow depths and where accurate details are required of thin strata. Two adjacent vertical faces could, of course, give accurate two-dimensional information such as "dip" and "strike," but for more than a few feet depth, the "trial pit" is uneconomical.

In the second method a borehole is drilled vertically downwards, either by rotary grinding or percussion, or a combination of both. The broken material ("tailings") is washed up to the surface by water which is pumped down through the centre of the drill. Careful examination of the tailings from each level, through a

---

*Excluding for the moment, seismic, sonic, and other geophysical methods of depth measurement, which are of very recent origin.

CHUNNEL

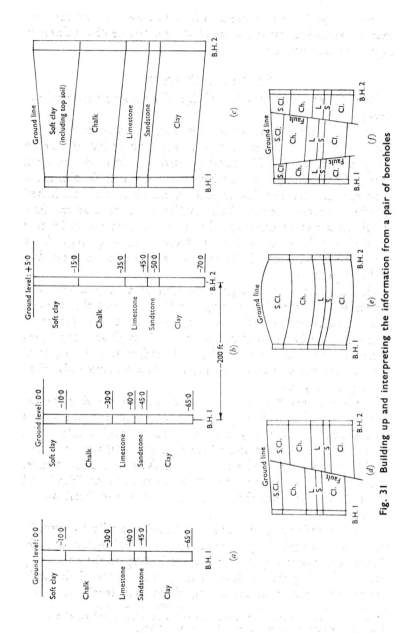

Fig. 31 Building up and interpreting the information from a pair of boreholes

92

microscope if necessary, gives an accurate description of the nature and thickness of the rocks through which the drill has bored.

The third method gives the most comprehensive information, for here we use a hollow tubular drill which cuts out an annulus leaving a central core.

This has to be brought to the surface in short lengths, but when these short lengths are laid end to end in the right order, they provide accurate visual evidence. They could, for instance, show that the first 10 feet of a borehole had been drilled through soft clay, the next 20 feet through chalk, the next 10 feet through limestone, the next 5 feet through sandstone, the next 20 feet through clay, and so on. These facts would be recorded diagrammatically as shown in Fig. 31 (*a*). If now we drill another cored borehole about 200 feet away and the cores revealed the same layers but at slightly different levels, we can add to our diagram, which might now look like Fig. 31 (*b*).

The next step—a tentative step—is to join the corresponding horizontal lines in this diagram, and the result is shown in Fig. 31 (*c*). These new lines ("horizons") give a first impression of how the various beds of rock slope downwards from their positions at the first borehole (BH.1) to levels 5 ft. lower at BH.2. We now have a two-dimensional picture, bounded by the top and bottom lines and the two boreholes, and it is tempting to think about delving into the third dimension.

But wait! Can we believe what we see? Of course not! The true picture could be as shown in Fig. 31 (*d*) or Fig. 31 (*e*), or even Fig. 31 (*f*).

All these variations are possible, although, within the distance shown, (*e*) and (*f*) are unlikely. The variation in the ground line can, of course, be seen and accurately plotted without any difficulty. But more information is required before we can eliminate (*d*), (*e*) and (*f*) and accept (*c*) as showing the true horizons. It can be obtained in several ways.

For example, there may be visual evidence of disturbance at ground level or just below. A trench is easy and cheap to dig, and, if its position is expertly chosen, could give valuable information of irregularity. Further boreholes along the line between BH.1 and BH.2 would give much more satisfactory proof, but boreholes are expensive. It should be remembered that, for the purpose of explanation, we have chosen a comparatively small, isolated zone of investigation; it is likely that a great deal is already known about adjacent and surrounding areas, and the geologist who is analysing our boreholes BH.1 and BH.2 has probably already a sufficient background of positive knowledge to enable him to decide if our Fig. 31 (c) gives a true picture.

Let us, then, accept our investigator's assurance that the horizons shown in Fig. 31c are reasonably accurate, and go on to the next step.

A third borehole, BH.3, placed so that the tops of the three holes form a triangle on the ground surface, will give us another and very important set of stratum levels, which may be as shown in Fig. 32a. If we now add the information in Fig. 32a to that in Fig. 31c, we can make a perspective drawing, Fig. 32b, which

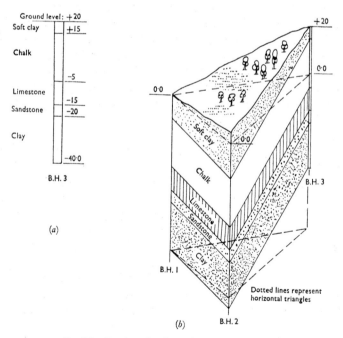

Fig. 32 Getting the three-dimensional picture

is, of course, subject to the same confirmation that we had to apply to Fig. 31c.

By drilling further boreholes, each of which forms a triangle with two previous ones, we can build up a three-dimensional view to any extent we require.

In fairness to the people who do this sort of work, two points should be made. First, the whole business is much more complicated than it has been made to appear, and a great deal of experience is required, both to make the correct deductions and to avoid the expense of unnecessary borings. Secondly, it is unlikely that, in an area known to consist largely of fairly regular sedimentary strata, the distances between boreholes would need to be as little as 200 ft. The actual distances would be very much greater, and only where analysis of the findings indicates irregularities would further intermediate bores be made.

By methods like this, many areas lying to landward of the British and French Channel Coasts have been thoroughly explored. Many of these explorations have been for quite different purposes. For example, the very thorough investigation of the geology of the Folkestone area was made with a view to developing underground water supplies. The findings and analysis of this and many other geological surveys have been pieced together rather like an immense three-dimensional jigsaw puzzle. The result is a very accurate picture of the rock formations underlying Sussex, Kent, and the North Coast of France, with a slightly less accurate picture of the formations under the Channel itself. But it is the latter with which we are now most concerned.

A great deal was learned about the sea-bed by the engineers of the nineteenth century, who were hammering away at the prospects of a Channel Tunnel, but from a very early date it had been known that the only feasible routes for a bored tunnel lay far below the zones which could be explored by scratching at the sea-bed. Samples of material brought up from the sea-bed had given some idea of the horizons of the various rock layers, but this only indicated the general run of those horizons at sea-bed level (the "out-crop interfaces"). Helpful as it was, this information was sketchy and insufficient until the middle of the twentieth century. So, in the late '50's, when the Channel

Tunnel Phoenix had arisen from its ashes for the umpteenth time, a very comprehensive geological study* was put in hand.

The investigators recruited the very latest techniques and the study was very thorough indeed. The inshore ground surveys followed the pattern already described, and included a detailed study of the microfossils occurring in one of the chalk layers. The land borings reached a depth of 615 ft. on the English side and 810 ft. on the French side, and the 4-in.-diameter cores provided abundant information. An interesting addition to these vertical bores was an inclined borehole put down from the end of the West Breakwater at Dover. Sloping outwards towards the sea, it was, in effect, a boring below the sea-bed.

The time was now ripe for the application to sea-bed survey of a set of techniques known as "geophysics," already well established for dry-land investigations. Of these techniques, what is known as the "seismic" method seemed to be the most promising for the investigation of the structure below the Channel bed. Two variations of the seismic survey method were considered. The first of these, known as the "standard refraction technique," was tried on land, to determine its suitability for the marine survey.

Seismic Survey by Refraction Method

The basis of this method is the fact that shock waves travel through different rocks with different velocities. A shock-wave can be propagated by means of a small explosive charge at a known point on the ground surface (or in a borehole). An instrument placed a known distance from that shocked point measures the time taken for the shock-wave to travel that distance. This is done first in a stretch of rock which has already been proved to be continuous and homogeneous. So, the shock-wave velocity in that type of rock can be calculated accurately. The same can be done for any other type of rock. From these calculations, a Table of shock-wave velocities for every type of rock can be compiled. (They range from less than 2,000 ft.

---

*The geological study was only one phase of the work of this important period in Channel Tunnel history. The whole range of technical problems connected with the Tunnel, as well as the financial, economic, legal, and political aspects, were subjected to intensive analysis and discussion.

per second for clay to more than 13,000 ft. per second for some of the harder volcanic rocks).

When the shock wave is sent through an unexplored zone, and the instruments indicate a velocity which differs from what it should be for uniform rock (as shown in the Table), then it is known immediately that there is a discontinuity. Experience, assisted by some rather complicated mathematics, can discover the position and nature of this discontinuity.

By the time it had been decided to apply seismic survey methods to the Channel Tunnel investigation, it was known that only one of the many rock layers beneath the Channel was of real interest. The survey was therefore aimed at discovering the upper and lower surfaces of this particular layer, and at proving its continuity. Unfortunately, in this particular type of rock and in those lying close to it, the differences in the shock-wave velocities were too small for the instrument readings to be reliable, and the method was deemed to be unsatisfactory for the undersea survey. It did, however, give some hope that the alternative reflexion technique would be more productive.

Seismic Survey by Reflexion Method

The method of echo-sounding for charting the bed of the sea is well known. The time taken for sound waves from the survey vessel to reach the sea-bed, and return to the vessel is measured accurately. And, since the velocity of sound waves through sea water is known, the depth can be calculated. If the sound impulses are repeated as the boat moves along, the return echos can be picked up by an instrument, which converts the time intervals into depths, and records them continuously on a chart. The same principle is used in the ASDIC apparatus which detects the presence, position, and distance of submarines in naval warfare.

The similarity of the seismic method is obvious, if we remember that sound waves are merely the mechanism by which energy is transmitted through air or water, or any other material. The energy waves produced by an explosion or an electric spark behave in exactly the same way. The term "shock-wave" can be used for all these methods of persuading some energy developed at one point to proceed in orderly fashion to another

G.   97 point. Now, the orderliness with which energy behaves when travelling in the disguise of a shock-wave is very important. First of all, the speed at which it travels is related to the density of the material, and secondly, it is a fundamental law of nature that any process which is running smoothly and without outside interference will carry on running smoothly, unless some change of conditions is forced upon it. Now, when a shock-wave, travelling through a uniformly dense rock, suddenly comes to a boundary between that rock and another, perhaps denser, kind of rock, it has to change its speed—and it objects! The greater the *change* of density, the more violent is the objection; that is to say, the greater is the change of energy. A reduction of speed is always accompanied by a reduction of energy—which has to find an outlet somewhere. The usual result is that a small, independent shock-wave is reflected from the boundary back to where the original shock came from. This can be picked up, and its energy and transit time measured by sensitive instruments, and every succeeding boundary through which the original shock wave has to pass will send back its own identity by means of a reflected shock wave. All these reflected shock-waves can be recorded by the same instrument.

The next step is to arrange for the impulse creating a shock-wave to be repeated in rapid succession, as the survey ship moves along; the resultant traces on the recording instrument's paper tape will look rather like a geological section. Indeed, after interpretation from "instrument language" into "geology language," they will be just that!

This method was first tried in the Channel using very-high-frequency impulses, each lasting for less than one thousandth of a second. With this very short duration of "buzz" a lot of energy could be put into each transmission.

A number of lines, totalling about six hundred miles, were surveyed by this means. In addition to the geological information obtained, this survey provided a contour map, which showed the rise and fall of the sea-bed at 6-foot intervals.

The method was successful in locating the edges of the outcrops (the interfaces) of the three most important rock layers. Reflecting boundaries could be traced downwards from the outcrop interfaces to a depth of about 30 yards and sometimes a little deeper.

But it did not go deep enough to tell us anything about the zone through which the tunnel would have to be drilled.

The next attempt used a much stronger shock-wave. This was produced by an electric discharge between electrodes below the water's surface. And since a much lower frequency was used, it was possible to pack a lot more energy into each impulse. The result was a much deeper penetration of the rocks, this time to more than 200 ft. below the sea-bed. This survey gave a great deal more geological information, and, furthermore, it clearly recorded the positions of faults which were already known, and so confirmed the Engineers' confidence in the method.

This was still not enough. For absolute certainty, we must know the conditions another 100 ft. down. But at least the seismic surveys have suggested the most likely positions in which boreholes will give the required information.

Boreholes at Sea

It had always been known, of course, that boreholes in the sea-bed would have to be made. For in the end this is the only method of getting really accurate information. Unfortunately, there were limits to the time and money which could be spent on the 1958/59 investigations, which we are now describing. Because of these limits, only eight boreholes were possible. The total length of all these was about 1,000 ft., and the deepest of them reached about 225 ft. below the sea-bed in 130 ft. of water. The same limits restricted the total length for which cores were obtained to about 50 ft.

The most satisfactory method of boring at sea requires that the drilling machinery be mounted on a stationary platform, which is rigidly held above the waves by stiff legs, resting on the firm sea-bottom. Such platforms had been in use for drilling at sea for both oil and coal prospecting. But they cost many hundreds of thousands of pounds, and none of those already existing was available at the time, nor likely to become available soon enough to be useful.

So floating craft had to be used, and the weather clerk made sure that the patience of the investigators was taxed to its limit, for during the total available time of 140 days, the water was too rough to permit work on 77 days, and the time required for setting buoys and moorings and for repairing some breakdowns left only 27 days for the actual boring programme.

Other restrictions which had to be observed were the need to avoid obstructing the four main shipping lanes, and to keep clear of the many wrecks lying on the sea-bed. Networks of communication cables also presented their own brand of problem.

Sampling the Top Layer

In the same way that a cake-knife so often messes up the layer of icing on top of the cake, so do the normal methods of boring prevent the true character of the top layer forming the sea-bed from being seen in its pristine condition, when the rock cores are brought up for examination. But it is very important to examine the outcrops of the rock layers, especially the layer through which the tunnel may be driven. De Gamond recognized this over a hundred years ago, when he indulged in his "bare skin diving" in quest of lumps of the sea-bed. So, in 1958, the investigators went after more samples for the same reasons, and in much the same way, except for the greater sophistication which attended a century of development in diving techniques, and a new outlook on palaeontology, which lays great value on the evidence of microscopically small fossils.

Diving, however, is an expensive business at any time, and the depth of water in the Channel is very near the limit of what can be undertaken by even the most skilled and intrepid of commercial divers. Preliminary attempts made in the shallower areas were so badly mauled by the weather conditions that diving for samples was abandoned in favour of a mechanical method operated from the surface.

A steel cylinder, weighing about 150 lb., with a sharp bottom edge, was dropped on to the sea-bed, In the same way that a gardener brings out a core of soil, in order to set a daffodil bulb beneath his lawn, so this sea-bed sampling tool brings up with it a piece of the sea-bed. But this tool was not heavy enough to make a worthwhile penetration, so it was changed for another nearly five times as heavy. Eventually, about three hundred useful samples were brought to the surface. Almost as many again had to be discarded, either because of uncertainty as to whether they actually came out of an out-cropping stratum rather than from a "foreign body" lying *on* the bottom, or because they were contaminated by the foreign matter in the sea-water with which they had been in such close contact for so long.

The main purpose of this sampling was to obtain confirmation and amplification of the information obtained by other means. In particular, the fossils in the chalk layers were minutely examined, and compared with the fossils in the chalk taken from the deep boreholes.

Fossilized Facts

The contribution which long-dead animals can make to engineering knowledge may reasonably be questioned by the uninitiated. It is very real, however.

To understand this, it is necessary to remember again that the beds of chalk were formed by the position of calcareous ($=$ mainly lime) materials from the sea. Each geological period of time, in which one distinguishable type of sediment is precipitated— later to harden into a sedimentary rock—is unimaginably long. So long, indeed, that it covers many biological cycles, in each of which a type of plant life or animal life has evolved, flourished, and become extinct. This process has provided geologists with an accurate measuring tool.

Fig. 33 explains this. In that diagram, the left-hand column represents a borehole log in which the twenty distinguishable layers of rock have been roughly grouped into a clay-type and two chalk-type complexes. (It is the middle group which is of special importance to the Channel Tunnel prospects).

To the right of this borehole log are shown highly magnified sketches of a few of the types of fossil remains which have been found and identified. All the fossils shown (and many more) are microscopically small, and they are collectively called "foraminiferida." Mention of typical species Anomalinoides globosa and Gavelinella balthica will perhaps be sufficient excuse for continuing this discussion in the most general of terms!

Now, if we think of the bands of the borehole log as representing very long periods of time, then the vertical lines (with arrowheads) attached to each of the fossils represent the periods of time during which each of the animal types existed in the prehistoric seas which covered this locality. But it is the depth through which

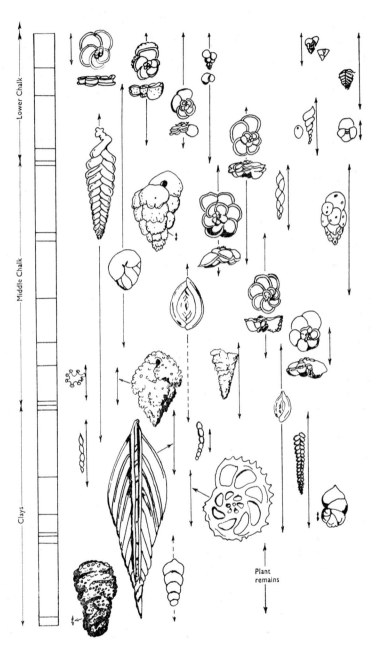

Fig. 33 Pictorial enlargement of some of the foraminifera found in the cretaceous zone. The vertical arrowed lines show the relative lengths of the periods of evolution of individual species of microfossil

each type of fossil persists that is of real importance. These fossil-band depths range from 6 ft. to 75 ft. Remembering that there are many more types, it will be clear that examination of all the foraminiferida found at any one level will give a very accurate location of that level, with respect to any specific level chosen to act as a reference datum.

This is important for several reasons. First, if a coring tool enters the sea-bed in the middle of an outcrop, the first fossils to be brought up will immediately identify which of the many layers of a generic rock type forms the bed-rock surface at that point. This helps in the location of the outcrop horizons between the various rock layers which are of importance in the investigation, and so we can make more accurate prediction of the most useful positions for further boreholes.

Secondly, fossil identification gives more accurately the levels at which one type of rock merges into another; visual examination of cores from boreholes cannot always determine these levels accurately, because, in many cases, the rock layers differ so little from each other in appearance that the transition zone may be very poorly exhibited.

Thirdly, the fossil data from several locations, when combined geometrically, will determine the exact dip of the strata in the area concerned.

Last, but not least, when actually tunnelling through a stratum, examination of the fossils taken from the working face will accurately determine the depth above and below the workings of the important interfaces. This is especially important where the dip of the stratum is greater than the allowable railway gradient, for when this occurs, there is a danger that the tunnel line will approach the upper or lower limit of the rock in which it is safe to work.

PUTTING TWO AND TWO TOGETHER

Now we have had a brief look at four methods of collecting data about the ingredients of our layer cake. Two of them deal superficially with the sea-bed; the other two go a lot deeper. It remains to put two and two together, flavour them with a study of the records of all past investigations, pop them into the oven of critical analysis, and see what result can be placed on the table of those who have to make the final decisions on construction methods and costs.

Although the investigations are still going on, it is possible to present a fair three-dimensional view of what these investigations are likely to confirm.

To understand the build-up of this picture, it must first be recalled that massive land movements in the far distant geological past have resulted in large areas of the earth's surface spending long periods alternately above sea level and below it. The area which includes Kent in England and the Boulonnais in France, and the Channel between them, is no exception. This area comprises what was once a single geological structure, shaped like an inverted oval dish. It arose in the Miocene Period of the Tertiary Era* as a by-product of the movement which caused the great Alpine upheaval in Central Europe. Table 1 gives an idea of the time scale to which the main types of rock are tied. (It should be pointed out that not all of the rock systems in the second column of the Table will occur at any one place).

But let us go back a long time before this inverted dish (or "Wealden Dome" as geologists call it) was first raised. The oldest sedimentary rocks in this complex are those of the Palaeozoic Era, which formed the base layers and were themselves partly eroded before the next layers were laid down by the sea which covered the area. Upon the Palaeozoic base were laid the rocks of the Mezozoic Era. In this area, the first layers of Mezozoic rocks were the Upper Jurassics. It was then that the floor rose (probably not for the first time) and the sea receded. Exposure to the weather resulted in erosion of the Jurassic rocks. In some places, the denudation was so complete that the upper layers of Jurassic rocks (the Purbeck and Portland Beds) disappeared completely. This is why the layer of Portland Stone, for which the middle reaches of the Channel are so well known, is missing altogether from the deeper layers between Dover and Calais. To the north-east, no Jurassic rocks remain in the rock layers beneath the south-east corner of the North Sea.

The sea again covered the whole of what is now Western

---

*The rocks of this "dome" structure were laid down in the Secondary (or Mezozoic) Era, and since it was above water level during the Miocene Period no rocks of that period occur in the dome.

Table 1

Era	Period	Approximate age of Rocks
Quaternary (The "Age of Man")	Neolithic Palaeolithic (or Pleistocene)	Up to 1,000,000 years
Tertiary (Cenozoic)	Pliocene Miocene Oligocene Eocene	Up to 60,000,000 years
Secondary (Mezozoic)	Cretaceous Jurassic Rhaetic Triassic	Up to 200,000,000 years
Primary (Palaeozoic)	Permian Carboniferous Devonian Silurian Ordovician Cambrian	Up to 500,000,000 years
Eozoic (before organic life)	Pre-Cambrian	Very old!

Europe and so came the long Cretaceous Period when the many layers of clay, sand, and chalk were laid down.

And so we come to the final stages. The "dome" heaved up, the sea receded leaving further deposits, like a monk's fringe round the lower slopes of the dome; and the cap of the dome was worn away before the latest localized settlement caused a number of small, irregular folds and faults and separated old

Albion from the less perfidious mainland and set for modern engineers the problems we are now trying to solve. (The actual date of the final formation of the present Channel is not accurately known).

The ideal illustration of the present condition would be a scale model with removable layers of papier maché, each coloured to represent a stratum of rock, but the covers of this book are too close together to permit inclusion of such an ambitious wad of paper. Fig. 34 will have to serve instead. The upper part of the diagram demonstrates how the wearing away of the crown of the dome has left elliptical bands of the different rocks out-

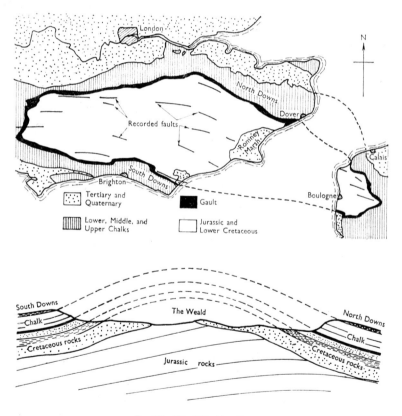

Fig. 34 The Wealden Dome

cropping at the surface. It does in fact show only one band, but all the others, if shown, would be concentric with the one we can see. The lower view is a very approximate cross-section across the dome as it appears landward of, and roughly parallel to, the English coastline.

And now we can look more closely at what is known and suspected about the narrow band across the channel through which the Tunnel must pass. It is in that narrow band that the various Chalk layers are at or near the surface. Fig. 35 shows

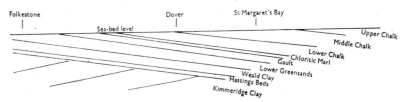

Fig. 35   Below the sea-bed near Dover (Slope of the rock layers is exaggerated for clarity)

the succession of the rock layers below the sea-bed near the English coast. It is not to scale and the slopes are very much exaggerated. It is merely a pointer as to what rocks are there, near Dover, and how they "dip" towards the North Sea as we move along the diagram from left to right. It shows too the order in which we could expect to find the outcrops as we move north-eastwards along the channel bed from a point opposite Folkestone.

There are three groups of chalk types, the Upper Chalk, the Middle Chalk, and the Lower Chalk. All these differ from the earlier rocks in that they are more homogeneous as a result of the less turbulent condition of the waters from which they were precipitated. They differ from each other only in minor characteristics intelligible to none but the geologist. Sufficient for us to say that they are slightly different in colour, hardness, permeability, and of course fossil content. It is the Lower Chalk which is most important. Its thickness ranges from 260 feet on the English side to 210 feet on the French side. It has a distinct clay content which contributes largely to its impermeability, and in the bottom 6 to 12 feet this clay dispersion thickens rapidly to change the nature of the chalk into what is called, among other names, Glauconitic Marl or more correctly Chloritic Marl. The rest of the Lower Chalk is very uniform but as the mud content slowly decreases from bottom to top, so the colour changes from the dirty grey, which gives it its alternative name of Grey Chalk, to a lighter grey. It is separated from the Middle Chalk by a thin band of dense clay which prevents the water so abundant in the Middle Chalk from percolating too freely downwards.

A second fortuitous band of clay divides the Lower Chalk into two sub-layers known as the Upper and Lower Cenomanian (Cénomanien is the name given by the French to the Lower Chalk) and affords a second line of defence against water percolation into the Lower Chalk.

And here is the crux of the whole matter. For the lower half of the Lower Chalk is the *only* layer of rock beneath the channel which has *all* the properties we require for the greatest speed, greatest safety, and greatest economy—all at once—for boring a Channel Tunnel.

Knowing this, we can now look intelligently at Fig. 36. The upper dotted line across the channel shows the path we would

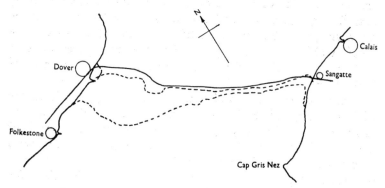

Fig. 36   The line of the tunnel related to the Lower Chalk

take if we could walk from England to France along the sea-bed placing our left foot always on the Middle Chalk and our right foot always on the Lower Chalk. The lower dotted line is the path of our return hike, also along the sea-bed but this time putting our right foot always on the Lower Chalk and our left foot on the next layer down, which is nearly always the Gault Clay but might occasionally be the Upper Greensand where this has not faded away. Remembering what we saw in Fig. 35 it becomes clear that these two dotted lines enclose the outcrop of the Lower Chalk on the sea-bed. If now we take a small part of Fig. 35 and flatten out the slope to something a little nearer reality we get Fig. 37. The small circle shows roughly the

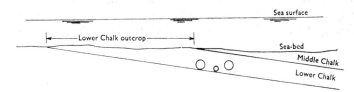

Fig. 37   Tunnel in the Lower Chalk

position of the tunnel if it is to be in the bottom of the Lower Chalk and not too near the sea-bed. Comparing this with Fig. 36 the tunnel centre-line will nearly always be north-east of the Lower Chalk/Middle Chalk outcrop interface. This is the main reason why the line likely to be chosen for the tunnel is shown approximately by the full line crossing the Channel in Fig. 36.

The reasoning which has led up to this tentative conclusion is based on information which has yet to be finally and accurately checked. That is one of the objects of the 1964/65 geological survey, which has yet to be completed and subjected to critical analysis. There may be some slight modifications before the exact line is fixed. For example it is already strongly suspected that at several places near the French coast the tunnel will have to come out of the Lower Chalk into the Middle Chalk and possibly into the Upper Chalk. It is also known that at least one major fault exists near the French coast, and that the tunnel *must* pass through it. At this fault the levels of corresponding rock layers differ by so many feet that there is little chance of keeping the tunnel within the lower half of the Lower Chalk. These are problems which the Channel tunnellers would prefer not to have to face, but knowing they exist, and where, is more than half the battle won. Modern techniques allied to experience will enable the tunnel to be driven safely through these danger areas, but the necessary precautions involve additional plant and materials, which are expensive. Each special obstacle to be surmounted will cause delay, which is also costly, for it puts back the date when revenues will begin to pay the bill.

All this can be allowed for in planning the work and estimating its cost, provided that every departure from straightforward continuous boring can be forecast. He would be a very confident man who would make such a prediction and there are many who say that no realistic figure could be quoted as a firm price, guaranteed free from increases as the work progressed.

CHAPTER TEN

So what?

*which is very un-basic English for " a discussion of
the basic features of design "*

BRASS TACKS

THIS IS perhaps the right place for a few fundamental questions.
First, what is "Civil Engineering"? Many definitions have been
attempted, some in very high-flown language. All the good
ones boil down to this: the aim of civil engineering is to change
the face of the earth at some place so that man can have more
of what he wants more easily than he could before the change.

How does the Channel Tunnel fit into this? It is believed
that it will make for easier, quicker, cheaper, and more comfortable
travel for people and goods between Britain and the Continent.
The belief has to be justified before the engineers can start even
the most tentative planning. The Channel Tunnel Study
Group has done just that. For it would be ridiculous to start
the technical planning of a project on this magnitude until the
following questions have been answered:—

(a) Will traffic expansion require Channel-crossing facilities
beyond those which could economically be provided by
expanding the existing air and sea services?

(b) Can sufficient money be borrowed to pay for its construction?

(c) Will the revenues from the forecast traffic repay the cost
(loan plus interest) leaving enough over to pay for staffing
and maintaining the Tunnel (and some profit eventually
for the financiers' great-grandchildren)?

(d) Can satisfactory legal and political agreements be concluded
between the countries concerned.

And, of course, the question we have already answered by saying,
"Yes, it can be done."

Now the questions (a) to (d) are outside the scope of this

book, but they are thoroughly dealt with in a publication by Her Majesty's Stationery Office entitled "Proposals for a Fixed Channel Link" (Cmnd 2137), which is a very readable document. It was published in October, 1963, but it was not until 6th February, 1964, that a decision was made at Government level that the "Fixed Channel Link" should be a tunnel for rail traffic only.

Whilst this was the first positive decision made for nearly a hundred years, it was also something of a blow to the motoring enthusiasts who liked the idea of driving themselves across the Channel, either by tunnel or bridge. This is not the place for polemics, but since we are going to talk about design problems it should be accepted that that decision was the only one economically wise.

And so we are led straight to the first questions the engineering designers really have to ask: what kind of traffic must the tunnel carry, and how much per hour? The answers are now well known. First, the traffic will consist of electrically operated railway trains, using three kinds of rolling stock—one for passengers only, one for passenger-carrying road vehicles, and one for goods.

The question of how much traffic per hour must be catered for has been the subject of an intensive study. The figures which have emerged from the study have the traditional vagueness of all traffic forecasts. But considering the great variety of factors which have to be taken into account, one can feel only admiration that the maximum and minimum values of the predicted traffic levels are so close as to be believable.

The process of forecasting was mathematically complex, but briefly it comprised making estimates for each of the years 1965, 1969, 1980, and 1985, for each of three main kinds of traffic:

Goods

Passengers without vehicles

Road vehicles with their passengers.

The likely totals of each were computed for a number of permutations of all the factors contributing to the growth of traffic using the present forms of cross-Channel transport, and an addition was made in each case for the traffic which would be generated solely by existence of the tunnel when built.*

---

*A parallel set of figures was produced for possible bridge traffic.

Earlier estimates had suggested traffic figures up to the year 2000 and beyond, but in the official proposals presented to Parliament by the Minister of Transport in October, 1963, the first seventeen years after opening the tunnel to traffic was considered the limit of time for which forecast figures could be considered reliable. Beyond that limit it was assumed that traffic would increase by 10% every five years until stability (saturation?) was reached about thirty years after opening.

It would serve no useful purpose to quote here the great mass of figures produced. The important forecast as far as we are concerned is that at peak periods in 1985* the maximum number of road vehicles per hour arriving at one end of the Tunnel would be about 1200.

Here was the first solid premise on which engineers could base their preliminary calculations.

It was quickly evident that a single railway track in each direction, using properly designed rolling stock and efficiently organized loading and offloading facilities, could cope with a peak hour traffic of 3,000 vehicles in each direction. This was far in excess of the estimate of "finally stabilized" traffic, and since one track in each direction was the minimum installation which could be considered anyway, we were all set to go.

THE SHAPE OF THINGS TO COME
Cross-wise

Having decided in previous chapters the approximate route the Tunnel must follow, the next question is the cross-section. We have already seen that the basic shape is circular. But how many circles? Do we try to put everything into a single tunnel, or is it better to have two smaller bores, one to carry traffic in each direction? Or more than two?

So long as there was a possibility of a highway in the Tunnel, the single-circle cross-section was not only feasible, but would have had to be of such dimensions that there would have been room for railway tracks beneath the roadway. But the cost of ventilation installations and the navigational obstructions caused by the islands that would have to be built in the Channel have

---

*It should be remembered that the 1963 assessment was based on completion of the Tunnel in 1969—which is now quite impossible.

vetoed the highway and we are left with the rather obvious fact
that two tunnels, each carrying one railway track, have a much
smaller total cross-sectional area than a single circular tunnel
large enough to carry two railway tracks. The total volume of
rock to be excavated is proportional to the cross-sectional area
and so the cost of excavation weighs heavily on the side of the
twin bore. Likewise, the lining of the larger single bore would
have to be much thicker than for the twin bores and comparison
of the total quantities of lining materials required again is in
favour of twin bores.

There are many other facets of comparison. For example,
the twin bores would require more but smaller tunnelling machines
than the single bore, and there is here an almost self-cancelling
disparity in capital outlay on plant.

We must consider too the greater difficulty of driving the larger
hole within the limits of depth of the Lower Chalk. The larger
the hole, the more chance there would be of hitting the top or
bottom of that layer.

The overriding factors are, however, the greater ease of driving
small bores and the smaller total volume of excavation; these
advantages of the twin bore are further enhanced by the fact
that the pilot tunnel, so necessary for exploration ahead, can
be drilled independently of the main tunnels, and can later
serve other useful purposes.

It is almost certain then, that if the Channel Tunnel is to be
bored beneath the sea-bed it will consist of three tunnels as
shown in Fig. 38. At frequent intervals along the length, they
will be connected by short transverse tunnels, as shown by the
dotted lines in Fig. 38.

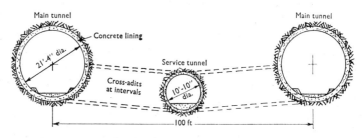

Fig. 38 Probable cross-section

The distances between the bores have been chosen as sufficient to avoid any overlapping of the zones around each heading where the stresses in the chalk are redistributed by the boring. Such interference would make rock-stress calculations almost impossible.

Lengthwise

The shape of the longitudinal section (the "profile") of the Tunnel is a little more difficult. The lower Chalk has already imposed upon us fairly strict limits on the depths at which we can dig. Nevertheless, the drainage problems in a tunnel 30 miles long cannot be ignored as a gesture of appeasement to Nature. It is of course believed that when the borings and linings are completed there will be no significant seepage of water into the Tunnel from the surrounding chalk. Even if this proves to be true we must not forget that trains will be carrying warm air from outside into a perpetually cool tunnel and there will be a continual build-up of condensation on the Tunnel walls, such as occurs on the inside of windows (car or house) on a cold day.

This problem is of course well-known in railways, and was particularly severe in days before electric trains began taking over from steam. For the railway tunnel passing under a hill the answer is easy. If the two ends (portals) are at sufficiently different levels, then the Tunnel can have a continuous slope from one end to the other, and the drainage channel let into the Tunnel floor does all that is required. (Fig. 39).

Where the difference of level is so slight that the resulting slope would not allow the draining water to flow away as quickly as it arises, the ease of setting out a straight tunnel has to be sacrificed. The Tunnel is made to rise from both ends until the two gradients meet a point within the hill called the "tunnel summit." This causes ventilation problems with which we are not concerned, but it does ensure proper drainage.

Clearly we cannot have this "gable profile" under mid-Channel with a "summit" higher than the portals. But wait! Many tunnels *have* been bored under water—and drained! The Mersey Railway Tunnel is perhaps the best example of what could be done on a larger scale under the Channel.

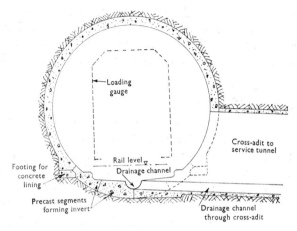

Loading
gauge

Cross-adit to
service tunnel

Footing for
concrete
lining

Rail level

Drainage channel

Precast segments
forming invert

Drainage channel
through cross-adit

Fig. 39   Drainage

Fig. 40 shows how the water draining down the two slopes of
the main tunnel is drawn off from the centre level portion by a
smaller tunnel, which runs alongside the main bore under the
middle of the river, but slopes *downwards* toward the Liverpool
and Birkenhead shorelines. It discharges into sumps at the
bottom of two inshore shafts and from there it is pumped to
the surface for disposal. This auxiliary tunnel and pumps can
cope with more than twice the usual inflow of 7-8,000 gallons
per minute, and also serves as part of the ventilating system.

Now the middle part of the Channel Tunnel will be much
longer than the middle part of the Mersey Tunnel. And, furthermore, it is possible, within the Lower Chalk, to give the tunnel
a slight downward slope in each direction from a point approximately half way. But this useful slope cannot be continued to
reach the shorelines without going too deep. The tunnel must
rise to the surface inshore on both sides. So we are left with
a very flat W-shaped profile, with the two lowest points each
collecting water from two legs of the W. From these points
small drainage tunnels can be drilled, sloping downwards to the
shorelines, where sumps, shafts, and pumps will complete the
task of draining the main tunnels.

For the length of the two middle legs of the W, the drainage

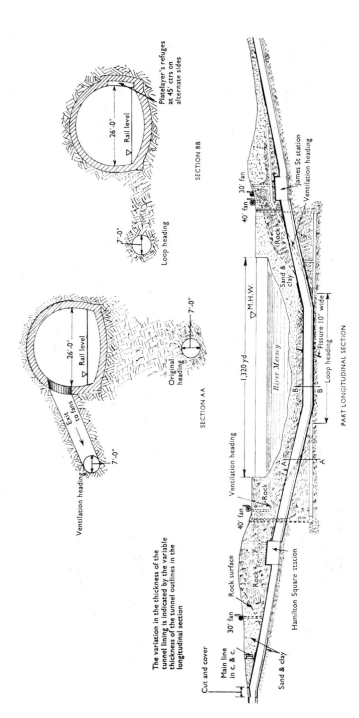

The variation in the thickness of the tunnel lining is indicated by the variable thickness of the tunnel outlines in the longitudinal section

Cut and cover

Main line in c. & c.

30' fan

Rock surface

Rock

Hamilton Square station

Sand & clay

Ventilation heading

SECTION AA

Exit to fans

Ventilation heading

7'-0"

26'-0"

Rail level

7'-0"

Original heading

SECTION BB

Loop heading

7'-0"

26'-0"

Rail level

Platelayer's refuges at 45' ctrs on alternate sides

1,320 yd

M.H.W.

River Mersey

40' fan

Rock

A   A

B   B

Ventilation heading

Loop heading

Fissure 10" wide

PART LONGITUDINAL SECTION

40' fan   30' fan

James St station

Ventilation heading

Sand & clay

Rock

Fig. 40   Mersey Railway Tunnel (vertical scale exaggerated)

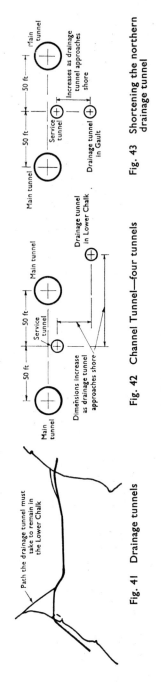

Fig. 41 Drainage tunnels

Fig. 42 Channel Tunnel—four tunnels

Fig. 43 Shortening the northern drainage tunnel

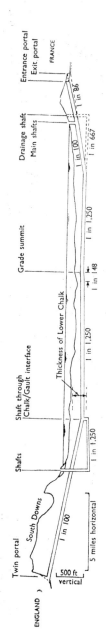

Fig. 44 Probable profile

water in the two main tunnels will run through interconnecting culverts (Fig. 39) into the pilot tunnel, which will everywhere be lower than the main ("running") tunnels.

At the ends, however, the drainage tunnels may not follow the line of the main tunnels and the pilot tunnel. The pilot tunnel, after all, must follow the same W as the main tunnels—or else it would not be "piloting" them. The drainage tunnels must, however, move still deeper as they leave the lowest points.

Now the Chalk layers "dip" towards the North Sea. So that if we wish to take advantage of the best possible rock conditions by following this dip with the end drainage tunnels they will have to diverge from the line of the main tunnels as they proceed shorewards and will reach the British and French Coasts at points to the north-east of where the main tunnels cross the coastlines (Fig. 41). On the French side, the dip of the Chalk is quite steep and if the low point of the W is fixed at about three miles from the coast the drainage shaft A would be quite close to the main working shaft B. The cross-section of the four tunnels would then be as shown in Fig. 42. On the English side, however, the Chalk layer dips much more gently and in order to follow it the drainage gallery would have to diverge more sharply and so would have to be much longer before it reached the coast-line. It would probably be more economical to accept the more difficult ground conditions and keep this drainage tunnel much shorter by following the line of the main tunnel as shown in cross-section in Fig. 43.

In this area the Gault is probably thick enough to accommodate the whole of the drainage tunnel, which will have to be shield driven. But the transition from the Lower Chalk to the Gault at the lowest point of the W is probably in difficult ground, and so it will be necessary to put a short vertical shaft down from that point into the Gault, so that the drainage tunnel could be driven in uniform conditions throughout its length.

In case all this sounds obvious and easy, it should be pointed out that the decisions on the lengths and slopes of the lengths of the W profile are based on the complex mathematical juggling of a number of basic factors. Put as simply as possible these are:

1. The Tunnel profile slope must never exceed the maximum gradient for the railway line as laid down by the operating

authorities (British Railways and Société Nationale des Chemins de Fers Française).

2. The Tunnel line must follow the Lower Chalk as far as possible.

3. The Tunnel must be as short as possible.

4. The gradient in the service (pilot) tunnel must be sufficiently steep to permit the drainage of all seepage water from all the tunnels.

5. The profile and position of working shafts must be compatible with the speediest and most economical methods of construction.

The unknown factor is, of course, the quantity of water which will seep into the workings during construction. Apart from short-lived excessive inrushes—which can, it is believed, be avoided—the total seepage is not expected to reach 110 gallons per second. (This figure has been adopted in design as the maximum seepage flow which can be permitted without adopting special measures described on pp. 136-7 as "forward grouting.") For the service tunnel to discharge this quantity without the water level rising high enough in the tunnel to become a nuisance it would have to have a slope of 1 in 1250.

Putting all these considerations together and compromising between those which pull in opposite directions, it has been shown that the tunnel profile and diameters cannot be very different from the layout shown in Fig. 44..

COMING UP FOR AIR

So far, our discussion has been mainly about the portion of the Tunnel which lies beneath the sea. Now we have to get up to the surface. So, to the geological problems we must now add the problems of the heights of land behind the coast and the connexions with the transport systems of England and France.

On the French side there is little difficulty, for three reasons. The land behind Sangatte, where the tunnel would cross the coast, is fairly flat and low-lying. So, the tunnel could rise to the surface as quickly as the maximum permissible gradient would allow. It so happens that it would emerge at a spot very near to

Calais, which is very convenient for linking up with the existing and proposed main Continental routes, both road and rail. Thirdly, it is fairly clear that the French end of the tunnel will have to come out of the Lower Chalk anyway, so there is no point in worrying about it.

On the English side the problem is somewhat different. The Tunnel will cross the coast beneath massive chalk cliffs, and, if it were to continue in its generally north-westerly direction, and at its maximum permissible gradient, it would have to go a very long way before emerging. Not only that, but it would leave the Lower Chalk, which is so important for economy and safety in excavation. We have decided that that is not significant in the short length between the French coast and the French portal, but there are so many miles to dig before getting clear of the White Cliffs of Dover, that any alternative route which permits continuity of driving technique is more than welcome.

For all these reasons, the tunnel, after passing under Dover Harbour, will have to turn sharply to the south-west and follow the Lower Chalk behind the coastline, until it outcrops just behind Folkestone. This exit (or entrance) is not a suitable place for the terminal area, which must be convenient for both road and rail connexions. It lies at the foot of an escarpment, and communication to the north is limited to the steeply-graded A260 road to Canterbury. To avoid this, and to make rail connexion, a surface line, which will still be part of the self-contained Tunnel complex, will run westward to a point near Westenhanger, where suitable road and rail interchange will be much easier to develop.

The terminals themselves will have to include facilities for the embarkation of passengers, the loading of road vehicles on to rail wagons, and the marshalling of rail goods vehicles into trains, which can run on both the British and French rail gauges (and through the tunnels of both countries). Provisions for customs and immigration checks will be somewhat similar to those at maritime terminals. These are all problems of traffic handling, and the design of the necessary facilities presents no difficulties, once the requirements are specified by the Operating Authorities.

So, we will get back to tunnel engineering.

KEEPING OUT THE UNWANTED

The first and obvious alien to be excluded from the tunnel is water, particularly the water which drips from the roof. We have seen that the total inflow will not be allowed to exceed 110 gallons per second, which seems quite a gush of water. However, spreading it over the total surface area of 30 miles of double tunnel and pilot tunnel gives an average seepage of about one pint per square yard per hour. Surely, this could be directed down the sides of the tunnel by means of a thin membrane over the roof, so that it could trickle away gently through the sumps? Why bother to line the tunnels at all? After all, we have chosen the Lower Chalk to be the host of our tunnelling machines, because it will stand unsupported after we have bored through it. And examination in 1958 of two of the three headings which were driven into the Lower Chalk in the late 19th Century showed little deterioration after nearly eighty years.

But we are forgetting something—the effect of pressure release or redistribution of rock stresses by boring (see page 88-9). This can result in distortion of the tunnel's shape, even in the firmest of rocks. Furthermore, if we were to put in only a thin water-proof lining the water which tries to seep in would merely build up a pressure all round the tunnel, which could be even more severe in its squeezing effect than the rock pressure. Now, the two existing headings which are below sea-level were deliberately flooded with water, after their abandonment in 1883, and so, since then, there has been an internal pressure to offset the external pressures which might have caused distortion. Furthermore, they were comparatively shallow, so the overburden pressures were not so severe as we may expect when we get deeper under the sea. And finally, those tunnels were only $6\frac{1}{2}$ feet in diameter, so their arch strength against outside pressure was much greater than it would be in the tunnels we propose, which are nearly four times as wide.

All this leads to the conclusion that we must line our tunnels very substantially, and the lining thickness will probably be of the order of 15 inches in the main tunnels and 6 inches in the service and drainage tunnels. It has been stated that this would be sufficient for the most severe combinations of rock and water pressures, although some engineers believe that the linings would need to be much thicker.

One final word about the invert linings. Because the rock pressure at great depth is the same all round the tunnel, the bottom lining would have to be the same thickness as the rest of it. But it is not considered necessary to make this bottom lining impervious because a little seepage of water through its joints would tend to relieve the hydrostatic pressure all round —rather like a built in safety valve!

FRESH AIR AND OTHER ODDMENTS

The question of ventilation is one of the major factors in the rejection of proposals for a highway tunnel. The cost of providing for the removal of the hot and foul exhaust gases from thousands of internal combustion engines was not justifiable when it was realized that the total forecast traffic could be carried by an electrically operated railway, producing no fumes.

The piston action of the electric trains running in tight-fitting tubes is well known, especially by those accustomed to waiting on the platforms of London's Underground. The trains push the air in front of them and draw different air along behind them. This at least creates a good circulation of air within the system, and so long as a little fresh air can be drawn in from outside to replace the oxygen used up by passengers breathing, the atmosphere in the underground is easily kept healthy.

In the Channel Tunnel, however, there will be a much greater distance between possible inlets and outlets and the trains will not fit the tube anything like so tightly as the trains of urban underground systems. On the other hand the proportion of the air vitiated by breathing to the total volume of air in the tunnel will be infinitesimal, and the rate at which it will have to be changed will be correspondingly small. Some artificial ventilation will be necessary, if only to allow for the possibility of occasional breakdowns or signalling delays, which might leave a crowded train standing in the tunnel for some time. There will therefore be a relatively small ventilation system operated by fans, but final details of what sort, how much, and where, have yet to be sorted out.

The "other oddments" consist of the railway track, electrical equipment for traction, lighting, and signalling, refuges for workmen, crossovers, etc. True, it is a little bland to class some of these very considerable works as "oddments", but all these other items are familiar to anyone who has travelled on a normal railway system with his eyes open.

CHAPTER ELEVEN

And how?

which asks tersely for a description of the methods which are most likely to be adopted for boring a Channel Tunnel

CATS IN BAGS

WE HAVE seen briefly all the basic techniques used for modern tunnelling. We have seen how the alignment of the Channel Tunnel has already been approximately decided and awaits only minor adjustment. We know what form the finished product must take. It remains now to weave into all this the special features of construction procedure which will have to be devised because of the sheer magnitude of the task.

But before attempting this, there is a limitation which must be accepted. A number of groups ("consortia") of civil engineering contractors have already spent much time and money in preparing detailed plans of how they would tackle this great work. They will soon, it is hoped, be keenly competing for the contract. Each will have different ideas on the best (cheapest)? way of attacking each facet of the project—boring, mucking out, lining, ventilating, draining etc. So it is unlikely that any one of them will divulge any improvement on presently known techniques which promises to give individual advantage at the tender stage.

Each of the processes will have many possible variants and to permute them so as to indicate every feasible plan in detail is clearly impossible. What follows therefore is a *pot-pourri* of fundamental procedures which can but represent a proposal which *would* work. In many cases the reader will recognize the possible alternatives. In other cases the alternatives will be mentioned.

THE PHONEY START

Everyone who believes in the Channel Tunnel is anxious to hear the command "dig." No doubt on the day after the word is given there will be an international fanfare of trumpets; high dignitaries will assemble, displaying their official robes and decorations; and one or more Prime Ministers, or perhaps a film star, or even a pop singer, will press a button or cut a tape or push a golden spade an inch into the ground. The job is on!

Cameras will click; speeches will resound over the site and later over the radio waves; Fleet Street presses will work overtime and Europe will be agog.

The bigwigs will go home again; the reporters will have exhausted their vocabularies of superlatives, and peace will reign again—especially at the hole in the ground where one would expect there to be the most frantic activity! A false start?

Not really a false start; only a symbolic display, or perhaps a prologue. No great civil engineering project can suddenly be projected into a feverish activity at the word "go." For although it can be assumed that the contractor, by the time a contract is awarded, has already formulated a plan of campaign, it is unlikely that the project manager will have risked purchasing the enormous quantities of plant and materials which he will eventually require.

When tendering for the contract it will have been necessary, among many other tasks, to investigate the availability of heavy engineering equipment, of constructional materials, and of skilled and unskilled labour. Unusual equipment will have had to be designed. The special services of many subcontractors, material suppliers, and plant manufacturers will have been bespoken. The time required for the delivery of the many kinds of plant and materials will have been related to the times when they will be required on the job. The availability of land for working areas and access to the work will have been pre-arranged. Not least, there must be assurance of the necessary funds which will be required for setting up the organization, for in work of this magnitude a contractor is involved in an enormous capital outlay before there is any return.

All this will have been planned by every contractor who has put in a tender. But until one of them has the signed contract documents safely in his strongroom, none can afford the risk of purchasing expensive equipment or hiring labour and standing them both idle while waiting hopefully to get the job. Of course large contractors will already possess some of the necessary equipment. But as much of it as possible will already be employed on other contracts, and its phased release from those jobs to the new work will have been planned. It will not be kept standing idle waiting.

So, at the word "go" there will indeed be a frantic activity, but it will be largely behind the scenes. In the office, thousands of conditional orders for machines and materials will be confirmed. Senior staff will be recruited, appointed, and redistributed from their existing tasks to their new responsibilities. Avenues of communications and collaboration between contractors and consulting engineers will be confirmed or established. Details of proposed construction methods will be re-examined, modified, refined. Thousands of drawings will be prepared. And then, no doubt, the consulting engineer who prepared the original designs on which the tender was based, will alter or modify his instructions, and much of the contractor's planning will have to be done again—in a hurry.

In the engineering works and factories, suppliers of materials and machines will be planning their production to meet the required delivery dates. And if there has been any long delay between the dates they made their promises for the purpose of tendering and the date of confirming the orders, the necessary replanning might indeed be of the "headache" category.

THE REAL START

Out on the site where the tunnel works are to start, the contractor will be setting up site office buildings, connecting up water and power supplies. Working space will have to be cleared. Access roads may have to be constructed. Plant maintenance workshops will soon be required.

And all the while this is going on the contractor's own geologists will be using all the time available to find every scrap of information which can possibly be of use.

All this is quite complicated enough when the main contractor is a single long-established company. But on work the size of the Channel Tunnel, many major contractors of different skills and experience will have to combine into a group or "consortium," probably by forming "a new company" to which each will second a number of senior staff, so that each different aspect of the work will be in the hands of an expert. The details of such collaboration will, of course, have been largely settled at the tender stage, but the "starting up" operation described above will not be any easier for that. In the early days, the scene at the works site would probably appear meaningless to those not directly involved. But it will settle down and after days, or weeks, or perhaps months, the "real" work of digging a big hole will be under way.

But it will not be simply a case of boring a hole in the ground somewhere in Kent and another somewhere near Calais and carrying on until they meet under the middle of the Channel. There is no doubt that that *could* be done, but the building of the Tunnel would take many more years than we could afford to wait for it. For example, if the tunnelling machines chosen for the job were boring at the rate of 70 to 80 feet per day (a reasonable figure, which will not be confirmed unless and until the work is actually being done) then two of them would need more than 3 years to meet at the middle. But that can happen only if the boring goes on 24 hours a day, 7 days a week, 52 weeks a year—which is not likely!

It might not be unreasonable to double that figure into 6 years. And remember too that the tunnelling machines—the "moles"—are massive and complex. They will have to be built to order, assembled, tested, taken to pieces for transport to site, reassembled. All this will take about a year. And when they have "holed through," the tunnel will be far from finished. Indeed we have so far considered only the digging of the pilot tunnel. Clearly then we must arrange to have more than two "moles" working. (We shall see later what arrangements can be made to ensure that work on both the main tunnels and the pilot (service) tunnel can proceed all at the same time.) So our first calculation would stipulate six moles working in six headings, but this we have already seen is too slow.

The first modification we can try depends on the fact that the total tunnel length of 32 miles comprises $6\frac{1}{2}$ miles under the South Downs in Kent, $23\frac{1}{2}$ miles under the Channel, and 2 miles under the French coast (these figures may vary slightly when the final alignment is settled). So if we were to dig vertically downwards, near the English Coast, to the depth of the tunnel line at that point, we could set two more moles to work in each of the pilot and main tunnels, one working landward and the other seaward. With the moles working from the French side the maximum distance to be travelled by any one machine will then be $\frac{1}{2}(23\frac{1}{2} + 2) = 12\frac{3}{4}$ miles, compared with the 16 miles of our first calculation. This gives a reduction of working time of 20%. Hardly good enough! A slight further reduction could be achieved by another shaft at the French coast line, and using the landward moles from the English side (after finishing their $6\frac{1}{2}$-mile stint) to do the 2 miles of the French landward drive. The transfer of moles would be expensive and the only result would be a shortening of each seaward drive by 1 mile.

Perhaps this is the point for the spirit of compromise to take over the computations and match the extra cost of shafts and additional machines against the economic advantages of shortening the construction time.

It has been suggested, perhaps drastically, that the time factor is sufficiently important to justify the building of an island at a suitable point in or near mid-Channel, where further shafts could be put down to tunnel level and another pair of machines installed in each bore. This would reduce the maximum driving distance for any one machine to about 6 miles. The time problem is now solved, but we are saddled with the cost of *fourteen** tunnelling machines, and an island.

It is unlikely that this would be an economic proposition, for these machines are likely to cost many hundreds of thousands of pounds each to build, even if they could all be built in time to start all at once. Furthermore, it would almost certainly be considered wise to have at least one extra machine, possibly two, available on standby in case of breakdown.

The next stage of compromise might be to move or resite the artificial island, with its three shafts to a point some distance from mid-Channel. This would break up the driving distance into unequal lengths and the moles could be juggled about so that some of them would work successively in two parts of the tunnel length. They would all finish their work at different times, but that would not matter much because those times could all

---

*Not fifteen, since it is unnecessary for the pilot tunnel to be continued landward from English coast line.

be phased in most economically with the procedure of lining, track laying, and other finishing installations.

Whatever is decided about this, the procedural plan would have to be adhered to, because all the different aspects of the following work would depend upon it.

GOING DOWN

Whatever arrangement of shafts is decided upon, it is certain that one of the earliest tasks will be the sinking of at least one vertical shaft near the two coast lines. They will be circular and large enough in diameter to provide access for all the men, materials, and machinery which are to be used down below, as well as the continuous power supply, water supply, and ventilation ducts which will follow the tunnellers as they drive.

These shafts will present no difficulty, for techniques of shaft sinking are second nature to all engineers who work below ground level. The ground is first cleared and levelled. The circle defining the shaft cross-section (including its lining) is set out on the surface and a shallow pit is excavated within this circle. Inside the wall of this pit are built a number of rings of lining. These may be iron, steel, or (more probably) reinforced concrete. Each ring will probably be made up from a number of pre-fabricated segments.

The number of lining rings to be erected initially in the pit will depend of course on how deep the pit can be dug without the walls collapsing. The firmer the topsoil the deeper the pit can be before digging has to be interrupted for the installation of the lining rings. If the soil is very unstable it is likely that one or more rings will have to be erected on the surface before excavation is started. Then all the soil is scooped out from inside the ring and the lining will sink under its own weight. More lining rings are built above ground level, more soil is scooped out, and the lining settles further. A point will be reached when the ground to be excavated becomes so firm and hard that the lining, which is now a large vertical tube, will not sink any farther under its own weight (even if assisted by heavy weights, or "kentledge," placed on top of it). At this juncture it becomes safe to dig the soil from under the bottom ring, inserting a new lining segment as soon as there is room to put it in place. The construction of the lining then continues by building downwards instead of upwards as in the early stages.

Any space between the earth and the outside of the lining rings is filled by grouting (i.e. pumping in a mixture of cement and sand in the form of a sloppy mortar).

There are many other methods of sinking shafts, dictated by the nature of the ground and the quantity of the groundwater. No real difficulty is expected to occur in the Chalk layers through which the Channel Tunnel working shafts will be drilled.

It is unlikely that these shafts will be down to tunnel level within some months of the date on which the contract is awarded. The shafts for the main tunnels will follow closely behind, because even before the main tunnel driving is well under way, there will be much coming and going of men and materials between the surface and the low level. Traffic jams cannot be permitted and all three shafts at each side will be fully used from the moment they are finished.

When the shafts for the pilot tunnel are down to the right level for starting the horizontal drives, it is expected that the first of many "mole" machines will be ready, but because of their length and method of operation they cannot be put to work until there is already a sufficient length of tunnel of the right diameter. So miners with hand-held pneumatic digging tools (known as "clay spades") will excavate landward and seaward from the bottom of the shaft, cutting out a sufficient length of accurately shaped tunnel in which to erect the mole. The machine will then be hoisted down the shaft, one component at a time, and erected in the hand-made tunnel. To make this easier, it is likely that the bottom of the shafts will be enlarged ("belled out") to give more working space for the machine erectors, and for subsequent operations of transferring materials between the vertical and horizontal haulage systems.

If it is eventually decided to open up additional working faces by having a set of shafts in the Channel bed, the sinking of these shafts would be a much more difficult operation. It has been done before but not in such deep water, nor in such severe wind and sea conditions.

Many of the schemes proposed in the nineteenth century included the provision of one or more islands in the Channel. But they were intended to be permanent, and in no case was a really practicable method of building them put forward. Building an artificial island in the sea has been done by depositing sand and clay on the bottom and building it up until it stands above water level. But this was in comparatively shallow water, and for the Channel depths the quantities of material required would be prohibitive. However, modern techniques used for drilling oil wells in deep water could come to our aid. The principle is well known; there can be few older readers who have not heard about the Mulberry Harbour pierheads at Arromanches in 1944 and the way they were held steady by winding spud legs down to the sea-bed and so partly lifting the landing stages out of the water. Younger folk will have read of the famous Texas Towers. These were enormous triangular steel pontoons fitted with great cylindrical steel legs, which could be jacked up and down at will. They were floated out to their positions at sea, the legs were jacked down until they were firmly embedded in the sea-floor. The jacking down then continued until the pontoons were raised clear of the highest waves and become stable platforms.

Fitted with radar gear for detecting unfriendly aircraft, and housing self-contained communities of men, these Texas Towers stood in the Atlantic Ocean for many years. Only recently (1964) was the last of them dismantled by blasting the legs off and beaching the platform for demolition.

Marine oil-well drilling rigs all over the world are now standing on their rigid stilts over deep water, providing stable work benches from which operations on the sea-bed can be safely carried out in all but the severest weather.

Such a contraption could easily be adapted to stand on the Channel floor. From it there could be lowered a large concrete tube, lengthened as it went down by rings of concrete placed on top, until it reached the sea-bed. Further lowering would be accomplished by excavating the sea-bed within the tube with mechanical grabs. When the tube had penetrated to the impervious Chalk the bottom edge would be sealed off with concrete and the water pumped out. The shaft would then be finished off "in the dry" down to tunnel level.

AND NOW—THE TUNNEL

It is unlikely that more than one or two "moles" will start work at the same time. Indeed it is unnecessary, for each will have a different length to drive and the planned starting times will be phased to suit the successive deliveries of the machines from their manufacturers. After all, the dates on which they *finish* are much more important and starting times will be planned to that "end."

There is no doubt however that the first mole to start will be in the service tunnel, for we must remember that in the early construction period, this will be the pilot tunnel.

The operation of the machine as a tunnelling tool has been described in Chapter 7. But one or two points still need mentioning here.

Pointing the Way

The road or railway builder has little difficulty in starting his machinery moving in the right direction. By means of a large-scale map, accurate drawings, a few surveying instruments, and some poles planted in the ground, he can lay out on the ground surface a sufficient number of visible guide marks to ensure that his progress is always in exactly the right direction.

The ocean navigator uses a chart and a compass, and after making allowance for wind and water currents he points his ship in the right direction and signals "full ahead" to the engine room. After a suitable interval he can check by means of a sextant, chronometer, and possibly by radio bearings, exactly where he is; and if, because of some inaccuracy he is not quite where he should be, he can alter his course so that the next leg of the journey will correct the error. If he makes his final landfall within a mile or two, it is good enough.

The tunneller has no such luck. He can see neither ahead nor to the sides. He has no beacons nor lighthouses to aim for. Magnetic compasses are not much good below ground. And he usually has to meet another tunneller coming from the opposite direction. Not only that, but the two must meet within inches! And if they don't, a whole lot of new problems arise.

The tunneller, then, must start off in exactly the right direction, and he must follow very accurately the line the tunnel must take.

A tunnel is rarely straight, and to add to the difficulty its path may have to change direction up and down as well as sideways. The curvature of the earth adds its quota of nuisance value; if the builders of the Channel Tunnel were to make no allowance for this curvature the tunnel would be a bridge by the time it reached mid-channel! On a more serious note: the tunnel would of course be laid out accurately in short carefully checked lengths and the real effect of the curvature would appear only in the notebooks of the setting-out engineers. They would have to make progressively larger corrections as the tunnel centre-line dipped further away from their shore-based horizon, until at mid-Channel, the overall adjustment for "curvature" would be about 150 feet. Clearly it cannot be ignored!

There are three main parts to the process of starting a tunnel along the right direction. These are:—

1. Setting out the "line" on the ground surface.

2. Transferring the direction of this line to the bottom of the shaft.

3. Making sure that the tunnel centre-line is in fact a true continuation of this line.

The first item presents no great difficulty and two markers can be set up at ground level, so that the line points in exactly the right direction. Two plumb lines can be lowered down the shaft, and provided they are absolutely stationary, a sighting line past the two wires at the bottom gives the right direction for starting the tunnel. But it must be remembered that the two plumbs are necessarily only a few feet apart, and any error arising will very soon multiply when the tunnel has gone a few hundred yards. Fortunately there are instruments available which will measure angles as small as three millionths of a right angle. This is so small an angle that the thickness of the plumb lines themselves gives rise to special problems in sighting the line.

The first few yards of each part of the Channel Tunnel will, as already explained, be dug by hand to make space for the erection of the machines. And so, before each machine starts boring, it will be possible to check back to the shaft by sighting along markers fixed in the roof of the starter heading. Subsequent checks will be made at frequent intervals. There are of course many complications, but they are all well known to tunnelling engineers and the reader need have no fear that the British tunnellers will come up in Belgium instead of France. After all, no contractor would contemplate so far deviating from his rendezvous in mid-Channel that he might end up by providing two tunnels for the price of one!

Keeping to it

Once the machine driving has got properly started in the right direction we must make sure that it keeps going in the right direction. Now these tunnelling machines are designed to be operated by one driver sitting at a consol from which, by switches and levers, he can control every operation of the machine. This includes the forces exerted by the lateral jacks which create the "purchase" against which the cutting head is shoved forward into the tunnel face. It is only by constant control and adjustment of these jack pressures that the machine can be "steered."

Stopping the machine every few yards in order to sight back on the markers and then making the necessary adjustments is not acceptable for several reasons. Corrections at intervals could result in the tunnel line being slightly zig-zag (although the deviation from the straight could be rendered insignificant by making the checks sufficiently frequent). Secondly, if the tunnel is to make a curve (as we know it must, several times, in both vertical and horizontal directions) the resulting path would be a series of straight lines instead of a smooth bend. Again the stoppages and checks would have to be very frequent, and thirdly any unnecessary stoppage or delay is the very negation of the principles on which these machines are designed; they are most efficient on long continuous driving.

Again there are many solutions to the problem. The most likely sounding technique is to harness a beam of light so that it is directed through accurately aligned tiny holes in the markers. By a system of mirrors and/or lenses installed on the tunnelling machine the light beam could be so directed that when the machine is in exactly the right orientation, a spot of light appears on a multi-ringed target which the machine driver can see constantly. Any deviation of the machine from its proper line would cause the light spot to tend to move away from the bull's eye; correction could be immediate, constant, and accurate.

When the machine has to negotiate a curve, the light beam can be bent by a carefully predetermined amount by adjustment of the mirror system, so that the operator's only concern is to keep the light-spot on the target centre.

There are difficulties in focusing light-beams in these conditions and it is possible that modern developments in laser beams can be harnessed more satisfactorily to this task.

Blind Man's Buff

And so we are off, feeling our way into the (largely) unknown. It is no longer necessary to stress the need for knowing what hazards lie ahead before the tunnelling machine encounters them. And in spite of all the modern techniques of ground investigation we can never be *quite sure* what the next turn of the wheel will find.   So we will put feelers ahead of the machine.

The tunnelling machines can be so constructed that when they are not turning, small-diameter drill rods can be put through the driving head and pushed quickly forward into the virgin rock for long distances. The material brought back by these drills will be reliable evidence of what lies ahead.   If they strike water, the inflow will be limited by the small diameter of the exploratory drill holes.

If the forward drilling finds no discontinuity in the chalk then the machine can go ahead again up to the limit of exploration.   But if there is evidence of water, or any other sort of ground, a well prepared emergency plan will be brought into operation.   This will consist in drilling a number of short holes in the tunnel face. (The machine may have to be brought some distance back from the face if the threat is severe enough to warrant extensive operations).

Glanded collars will be fitted to these holes and drills will be pushed through the glands so that the water can no longer enter the tunnel.   Long holes will be drilled into the ground ahead of the workings and they will be directed so that they diverge slightly outwards in all directions from the tunnel line.   The drill rods will then be withdrawn and replaced by grout pipes, through which a cement slurry will be pumped at high pressure. This will not only fill the drill holes, but will percolate into the previous ground until the future path of the tunnel and some of the space around will be completely permeated. After a waiting period for the cement to harden, driving can restart and continue to the extent of the consolidated ground.

There are two possible refinements to this method which should be mentioned. First, if the unsatisfactory conditions found by the exploratory drilling are not too severe, it may not be necessary to use cement, which after all is expensive and which also may result in the ground so treated becoming harder than the chalk for which the tunnelling machine was designed and equipped. It may be possible to replace a large part, or all of the cement by a finely divided clay, which will clog the interstices in the bad ground and so render it amenable to tunnelling. There is also a possible use for thixotropic materials.

The second refinement concerns the method of forward exploratory drilling. If this has to be done through the machine head, the machine cannot be driving at the same time. But we have already decided that the machine must be kept going as continuously as possible. Stoppages for drilling which finds nothing would be doubly exasperating. So we must look for a way of exploring ahead without stopping the drive. This can be done by excavating pockets at the sides of the pilot tunnel large enough to house the necessary equipment for drilling long forward holes. One such hole will be drilled on each side of the pilot tunnel, one slanting slightly upwards and one slightly downwards—for obvious reasons. These drills will advance much more rapidly than the mole, so it will be possible to explore a long way ahead, withdraw the drill, excavate a new cubby hole, and start drilling again, long before the machine has reached the limit of the last test hole.

In this way the machine can be kept constantly at work so long as no trouble lies ahead.

Most important of all, this technique permits the driving of main tunnels to follow closely behind that of the pilot tunnel, instead of having to wait until the pilot has fully explored the whole route across the Channel.

THE FINISHING TOUCHES

The lining procedure will depend upon the type of lining to be used. There may be places where it will be deemed wise to use the more expensive cast-iron or steel segments, but generally it may be expected that the lining will be concrete. The methods of concrete lining have already been described.

Since the lining need not follow the moles very closely, the work can be separately planned and phased to suit the most economical use of the equipment. There is no doubt that every possible degree of mechanization will be pressed into service. For installing precast segments there are machines already in use which will pick up the segments, place them on a hydraulically or electrically operated arm, and press them into position, holding a complete ring of segments until the keystone is fixed in the crown to complete the arch.

Laying the rail track and installing power supply and signalling equipment will follow long-established practice and present no unusual problems.

And here we must end the "boring tale," for although there are many other bits and pieces which go to make up the whole exciting prospect, there is another and completely different story yet to be told.

PART THREE

The end of an adolescence

*which means to say that the comparatively new
technique of subaqueous tunnelling by laying
prefabricated tubes in a submarine trench
is now an established practice*

CHAPTER TWELVE

From pipe dream to practicality

*in which are mentioned some early developments and
the basic requirements for immersed-tube tunnels*

FROM BABYLON TO BOSTON

THE "BORING TALE" is ended, and what a long tale it was! But
the art of digging holes under the ground is as old as mankind;
it is not surprising therefore that it has reached such a state of
sophistication that modern engineers can bore a tunnel *anywhere*
if they *want* to (and if someone can pay for it!). Countless
thousands of examples, large and small, give testimony to the
steady advance of this sophistication.

What might, on first thoughts, be surprising is the fact that
a comparatively callow youth among tunnelling techniques should
be under serious consideration for such a testing of adulthood
as the Channel Tunnel.

So far, less than forty tunnels of the so-called "immersed
tube" type* have been built. This seems an impertinently
small number to offer as experience competing with the wealth
of boring "know-how." But the figures should be put into
perspective, and when compared with the number of existing
under-water tunnels, the number of immersed tubes is much
healthier. The proportion is growing rapidly. In North
America particularly, wherever a water crossing can be effected
by both types of tunnel, the immersed-tube technique is rapidly
gaining on its elder brother.

---

*The Author considers this nomenclature to be imprecise. There are
several less ambiguous ways of describing the technique, but "immersed tube"
is most commonly used by engineers, and since it has also the merit of brevity,
it will be "admitted" in what follows.

Date of Birth Unknown

How did it all start and when?

It has been suggested by a Sicilian historian, Diodemus Siculas, that Semiramis, Queen of Babylon, expressed a wish to be able to cross the Euphrates from the royal palace to the temple of Jupiter Balos at any time without getting her feet wet. The story goes that her obedient engineer built a tunnel more than 3,000 feet long. During the season of low river-flow an embankment thrust the river out of its usual course, and in the dried-out bed he erected a continuous brick arch, sealing it with hot asphalt. Demolition of the embankment returned the river to its original course and the tunnel became effective as a dry river crossing.

There is no real evidence that this tale is true. The almost shapeless remains of what was once a man-made structure, possibly 2,500 years old (which tallies), helps the imaginative to give credence to the story, but it is unlikely that twentieth century engineers will concede the Babylonians a 25-century lead!

So, rather reluctantly, we must dismiss the historical sentiment that the immersed-tube tunnel was born in Babylon. It is more reasonable to think that water-supply pipes laid across the beds of shallow rivers were the immersed-tube embryo in the fertile womb of Roman military and civil engineering.

And for eighteen centuries there is no story of tunnels under water. The first to be documented was the Wapping-to-Rotherhithe tunnel under the Thames, started in 1825. It was driven inside a shield which, although naïve by modern standards was a marvel of its time. This is not the place to discuss the difficulties and disasters attending that work. It was eventually completed and has its place in history as the forerunner of a series of shield-driven subaqueous tunnels in the nineteenth century.

Although the shield technique was developed and perfected as described in Chapter 6, it remained expensive and every subaqueous tunnel of the period confirmed the view that the only way of finding out the real geological conditions beneath the sea- or river-bed is to get down there and see them. But towards the end of the century a tunnel, now little remembered, was built for the Boston Metropolitan sewage works. Known as the Shirley Gut Siphon, it was of no remarkable magnitude.

The tunnel itself was 1,500 feet long but the width of the river it crossed was only 315 feet. It was made of 8-foot-5-inch-diameter steel tubes, lined with brickwork to an inside diameter of about 6 feet. Lengths of 48 feet (and some of 68 feet) were laid on the river-bed and joined, leaving a navigation depth of 25 feet.

Although a far cry from the dimensions of the English Channel, this insignificant job in Boston, in 1893, heralded a new era in subaqueous tunnelling. For although the true birthdate of the idea is unknown, this was the first practical application to an underwater bed-level tube large enough to be called a tunnel.* It was in fact a somewhat hesitant herald for there was a break of 18 years before the next example was attempted.

RULES OF THE GAME DEVELOP

The babe cut its teeth in 1911 when the Detroit River was spanned by a railway tunnel nearly 8,400 feet long (although the distance between river banks was less than 3,000 feet). This was the first† transport tunnel of the immersed-tube type, yet it embodied many features which have appeared over and over again since with but little modification. To this extent it might be said that the development of the technique was sudden and complete when the Detroit River Tunnel was finished. But, of course, as more and more water crossings were tackled, new problems of width, depth, water-surface conditions, and navigational restrictions required refinements in the design and construction methods.

There are a number of basic requirements which have to be satisfied in the design and construction of all immersed-tube tunnels. They are so fundamental that they are common to practically all such tunnels so far built. The very few departures

---

*There is no universally accepted diameter at which a pipe or tube becomes a tunnel. It might be considered reasonable to suggest that it is the smallest diameter in which a man can perform an operation related to its building. This would be anywhere in the range 2 feet to 3 feet.

†The Author was recently reminded of three tunnels under the Seine in Paris, built about this time. At least one of them was completed before 1911. They were constructed by three closely similar methods, all of which marginally resemble the technique about to be described. But in the Author's opinion the resemblance is not close enough to rob the Detroit tunnel of the honour here accorded to it.

from these guiding principles have arisen from very special circumstances.

First it must be remembered that the geographical situation in which an underwater crossing for traffic is needed is invariably one in which the existence of the waterway has itself led to industrial development of the type which requires shipping to use the waterway. The navigation channel must therefore be preserved at the width and depth required, not only for the existing maritime traffic, but also for future shipping developments. There are few estuary ports where the water depth remains ample without dredging or channel-training works of some sort. This suggests right away that we must leave no significant projection above the sea—or river-bed which can constitute a danger to either the keel of a ship or the tunnel itself.

So the first requirement is a trench in which to lay the prefabricated tunnel sections. But that is not all. The tunnel must be protected against the possibility of a ship sinking on top of it. The trench must therefore be deep enough for the tunnel to be covered with a protective layer of material, sufficiently thick to absorb the shock of a foundering vessel and to distribute the resulting stresses in the ground so widely that by the time they reach the tunnel structure they can do it no harm. Ideally, for this purpose, the covering material ("backfill") should be fine-grained, but this is possible only in conditions where there is little or no current or tidal flow of the water near the bed which would wash away the protecting cover. The backfill must therefore be of large enough pieces to stay put, and a compromise must be reached on the basis of maximum current speed—and this must of course be carefully measured before planning can begin.

In the few cases where these questions can be ignored there is ample depth of water, and the usual corollary to this is that water movement on the sea-bed is of such a low velocity that "scour" is unlikely.

The second fundamental requirement is that the bottom of the tunnel, when dug, will support the tunnel sections without subsequent settlement—especially differential settlement, which would throw insupportable stresses on the joints between the tunnel sections. This problem is not so severe as it sounds, for, after all, the tunnel is hollow, and although a prefabricated section such as proposed for the Channel Tunnel might have a dead weight of 20,000 tons, a very large proportion of this will be offset by the buoyancy, leaving very little weight to be supported. The area supporting it is so large that the load on each square foot of the trench bottom will be less than 500 lb. Remembering the efficiency of quite a small wooden plank in saving a man caught in quicksand or bog, it is easy to see that the bed material would be very poor stuff indeed if our tunnel section were to sink into it. Indeed, if it were that bad, it is unlikely that a trench could be dug into it anyway, for the sides would collapse as quickly as the stuff was excavated.

The next point is that the prefabricated units forming the tunnel should be as long as possible to reduce the number of sinking and jointing operations. But at the same time they must not be too long to handle. Handling includes: launching or floating them off the stocks where they are built (either on slipway or in dry-dock); towing to temporary berths for installation of auxiliary equipment and possibly for storage until they are wanted; towing to their final locations; controlled lowering to the sea- or river-bed. During the towing process, wind and wave can produce severe distorting stresses and if the unit is too long it will be insufficiently stiff to withstand these stresses without damage.

Fourthly, at all stages of construction when the tunnel unit is afloat, it must be stable. It must float straight and level, for any tilt, lengthwise or sideways, would make control difficult, especially when lowering is about to start.

Number five is the need for a system of sinking the tube sections so that:

(a) They are in the right place before sinking starts.
(b) They are under complete control while sinking.
(c) They are in the right place when sunk.

It is here that the growing pains of immersed-tube-tunnel development have been most persistent.

Most important of all from the point of view of safety, although sixth in our list of fundamentals, the joints between the sections must be watertight. And this must be achieved even when some slight degree of flexibility is required.

And lastly it must be remembered that the sunken tube must be connected to the dry-land portion of the tunnel by transition sections, which, although below water, are in a depth too shallow to permit the float-out-and-sink technique.

All these problems have been solved, in many different ways. We shall now examine some of the solutions devised for the immersed-tube tunnels already built and see if and how they could be applied to the Channel Tunnel. For this project will present problems at every stage which will be at least as difficult as any that have gone before.

CHAPTER THIRTEEN

The big dig

which is basic English for "the excavation of a long deep trench in the sea-bed"

SORTING OUT THE SEA-BED

THE SEA-SIDE holiday maker knows perfectly well what the sea-bed is like. He can see for himself how the sandy shore slopes down beneath the waves and there is no obvious reason why it should change. But of course, this is not the whole picture. The golden yellow sands so beloved of the children are the result of progressive grinding down from rocks to pebbles to gravel, etc., by wind and wave action which occur just above, just below and within the tidal range.

Even within this range there are wide variations in the fineness of the beach material. It can vary from coarse shingle, which the water seldom reaches, through fine sand, where the grinding action is heaviest and most frequent, to coarse shingle again at the lowest tide levels. And in deep water, where the bed is little disturbed by tide or current there may be almost anything from solid rock to the finest of silt. Where there are no major coastwise currents, but merely to-ing and fro-ing of the tide, the finer particles of grit removed from the sea shore will gradually settle and form a soft, perhaps muddy, bed. It is rarely "golden sand."

At the mouth of a fast-flowing river, the bed may be scoured clean of deposit. In an estuary which fans out rapidly, the river water will quickly lose its silt-carrying capacity and will drop what is called the "bed load." There is usually a considerable depth of alluvium in river mouths and estuaries.

It follows that the procedure of digging a trench for an immersed-tube tunnel is by no means stereotyped.

SHAPING THE DITCH

It is very important to decide at an early stage on the most economical shape of the trench cross-section. This is related to the size of the prefabricated tunnel units and to the cohesiveness of the bed material. The slope of the trench sides must be somewhat less than the "angle of repose"—a term which may need explanation:—

If stones are heaped into a conical pile, shovelful by shovelful, a point is soon reached when further stones dropped on the top merely run down the sides to the bottom. They will form a circular bench round the base of the pile. Further shovelfuls will run down to this bench and the pile can only grow higher in the sequence shown in Fig. 45. It will be seen that the slope of the pile in (*f*) is the same as that in (*c*). This will repeat if the process is taken further, and there is always a maximum steepness of the slope at which the stones will stay put without rolling down.

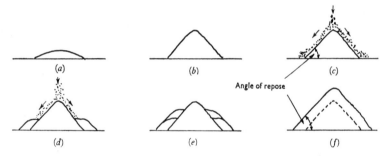

Fig. 45   Pile in repose.   Steps in the building of a conical pile of loose material

The same sort of thing will happen if one shovels dry sand into a conical pile, but the maximum slope will be different. If the sand is damp, the slope will be steeper (as every child knows who up-ends a bucket of sand). This maximum slope at which the piled up material will stay put is called "the angle of repose," and it is different for every type and condition of material.

The same principle works in reverse. If we dig a trench, and leave a side of it sloping more steeply than the natural "angle of repose" for the material, then the trench side will fall in, as in Fig. 46.

Now we can look at two possible cross-sections (Fig. 47) which both give a width of say 60 feet at the bottom of the trench and a depth of 40 feet. Let us suppose that in (*a*) the angle of 60° represents the "angle of repose" for the bed sand. Clearly it would be dangerous to dig to exactly that angle. What margin should be allowed? It is just too easy to say "let's play safe."

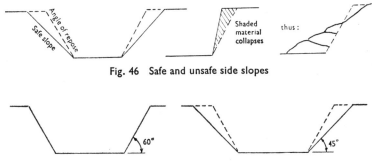

Fig. 46   Safe and unsafe side slopes

Fig. 47   The cost of playing safe

Suppose for instance (and for safety play) a slope of 45° was chosen (Fig. 47 (*b*)). Now remembering that our trench across the Channel is going to be more than 20 miles long, the extra material to be removed if we are to get (*b*) instead of (*a*) amounts to nearly 2 million cubic yards. That sounds like an awful lot of money to spend on unnecessary dredging. The decision on what allowance to make beyond the angle of repose will be based first on an accurate investigation of the bed material and secondly on a vast experience of dredging and its associated problems.

It is known, and may be considered fortunate that the bed of the Channel is largely firm Chalk throughout the likely route of the Tunnel, probably because the fast currents through the narrows of the Dover Strait have scoured the sea-bed clean. This Chalk will stand unsupported at very steep slopes. It would be unwise to expect it to stand vertically, for the trench will in some places be more than 50 feet deep, and the behaviour of a newly exposed chalk wall of this height is problematic. It is fairly certain however that there will be reasonable economy in the total material to be dredged.

But here arises one of those exasperating paradoxes which so frequently confront the civil engineer, whose life is one long compromise with nature. The softer the bed material, the easier it is to dredge. Harder materials require tougher and more expensive plant. And if we meet any hard rock which has to be blasted out, the costs will really mount up.

Let us remind ourselves of the size of this dredging task. The figure of 2 million cubic yards quoted above referred only to a difference between two possible excavation volumes. The trench dimensions chosen as an example to illustrate this difference are not unlike those of the trench which will be required for the Channel Tunnel. The total volume of excavation will far exceed 10,000,000 cubic yards. Clearly this is a man-size task in any conditions. So bearing in mind the severe depth, wind, and wave conditions in the Channel we must choose our dredging equipment very carefully and be sure that it will stand up to the job, whilst removing the material quickly but cheaply.

The type of dredger which uses an endless chain of buckets, operating like an escalator, is well known and needs no description. It is a sturdy machine which will cut quite hard material. When working smoothly it can produce enormous output. But it should be remembered that the "ladder" holding a great weight of buckets and driving machinery has to be pivotally mounted on a floating craft, probe deep down into the sea-bed, and yet exert a great cutting pressure on the bed material. The stresses set up in the ladder mountings by this action, are multiplied when there are also wind and waves. Striking an unexpectedly hard pocket could cause disaster. And no such dredger could give satisfactory service in the depth of choppy water which extends most of the way across the Channel.

Another well-known excavating machine, which is also commonly seen on land, is the "grab." This consists of two half-buckets hinged together so that as the jaws are closed the two edges of the half-buckets bite into the ground. When the teeth meet the machine has a "mouthful" of earth which is whisked away by a crane. The same principle is used in marine dredging, and with suitably weighted buckets and specially hardened teeth on the bucket edges, this grab-type dredger can deal with quite hard material. But in deep water, taking only one bite at a time, with long periods of winching up and down between bites, it is a slow process—think of 10,000,000 cubic yards! Furthermore it would be very difficult to dig our trench to an accurate cross-section; the bottom, particularly, would be very uneven, and additional expense would be incurred in levelling it again by putting graded material back into the hollows.

Both grab and bucket-chain dredgers require an attendant fleet of barges to carry away the dredged material, and these must be taken into account when considering both cost and the difficulty of working on a choppy sea.

The straightforward suction-type dredger works somewhat like a vacuum cleaner (a scientifically incorrect but well understood terminology). Whilst the carpet cleaner uses moving air to carry away the dust, so the suction dredger pumps water into its snout, and the water carries the loose material with it up to the surface for disposal. Provided that the bed material is amenable to this treatment, the suction dredger (and its derivatives) have an advantage over dredgers which carve lumps out of the sea-bed; for the piping which carries the muck away can usually be extended so that it also deposits the muck in a place where it can be of some use—backfilling or reclamation. The Channel bed material is, however, too hard to take advantage of this.

It would be little use either to try a suction-dredging system by first breaking the surface material with a strong pressure jet, for such jets could have little effect at 200 feet depth. And there is the added disadvantage that a high-pressure jet would so stir up the soup that any subsequent operation which required supervision either by diver or closed-circuit television would be impossible for a long time. Even the dimensions of the trench as dug could not be measured until long after the dredger had moved on.

There is another kind of dredging equipment which promises to be just the ticket, if properly adapted. This is known as the cutter-head suction dredger. It has been in common use for a long time in a wide range of sizes and seems almost to have been waiting for the Channel Tunnel to start in order to show what it can really do.

Roughly the principle of this dredging tool is a combination of cutting and pumping. A series of heavy steel curved knives are mounted on a rotating spindle in such a way that they look rather like a globe built up of crescent moons. As this globular head turns, the knives chisel out a bench with a curved back. The cutter is mounted on a pivoted arm so that it can be swung horizontally in a semicircular arc, and the bench so formed is about half the depth of the cutter head. The arm carrying the cutter can then be lowered by that depth and a further semi-circular sweep will double the depth of the bench—and so on. When the benching has reached the required depth (Fig. 48),

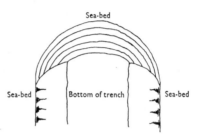

Fig. 48 Benching the trench (The working face is kept at the same slope as the trench sides (= angle of repose plus safety allowance.) Then one series of dredged benches from top to bottom of the face advances the trench by the width of one bench)

the cutter head is returned to the top level, and the whole dredger is moved forward to start the next cut.

The arm which carries the cutting head can also carry a pipe through which water is pumped to carry the excavated material to the water surface for disposal. The cutting head itself is a compact and efficient unit, easily driven through long rotating shafts and universal joints. The arm which carries it can be of much lighter construction than the ladder of the bucket-chain dredger. The result is that modern rotary cutter heads can be mounted on long booms and so can reach into deeper water than ever before when installed in floating craft. They have recently been used in depths approaching those of the Channel. But this was in calm water and in good weather. And it is still not possible to consider using even this most efficient development of dredger types from floating craft in the Channel. The slightest wave movement at the surface will magnify itself along the boom to the cutter head and could cause a great deal of trouble.

What then, are we to do? We have a dredging implement which will do the job and cut away the chalk of the Channel bed efficiently, if only we can give it rigid support from which to work. There is a solution, but we must do some more exploring of techniques before we come to it.

ISLANDS IN THE AIR

Now it is time to have a closer look at those platforms on stilts which were mentioned briefly in Chapter 11 (p. 132). The Mulberry pierheads at Arromanches in 1944 were probably the first structures of this kind to receive the accolade of public acknowledgement. One of Churchill's most publicized pronouncements concerned the conception of these accessories to the Normandy landings. When discussing the possibility of these landings in 1942, Churchill had foreseen the need for taking a prefabricated harbour over the Channel and setting it down near the French coast so that heavy equipment could be landed in close support of the infantry and airborne assault.

In a typed minute to the Chief of Combined Operations in May 1942 he succinctly dismissed the feasibility of all landing-pier types known at that time. He added a handwritten footnote:

"They *must* float up and down with the tide. The anchor problem must be mastered. The ships . . . Don't argue the matter. The difficulties will argue for themselves."

It is a common belief that this postscript gave birth to the idea of the spud pontoons used in the construction of Mulberry Harbour. Sir Winston himself would not claim to have invented them. Nevertheless his words showed a complete grasp of the extent to which the existing techniques would fall short of requirements. Perhaps the most important words in that missive were "The difficulties will argue for themselves." Indeed they did, and so to some extent did the solution. For the principle of the spud leg was already well known and the final design of the semi-floating pierheads clearly owed a great deal to the Lobnitz type of spud-leg dredger which had long been in use. The conditions of operation were of course much more severe than any which had been formerly envisaged.

However, and whenever, the idea was born, it was to go through much development before the Channel was again to claim its attention.

Why can we not repeat Mulberry? In the first place those stagings were not meant to be moved about on the sea-bed. Once in position they stayed there. Secondly they were designed to provide berthings for ships which would exert heavy horizontal forces on them. So they had to be flexible and absorb shock by moving under impact. To achieve all this most economically it was arranged that when the legs were winched down to the sea-bed, the platform was lifted only a few feet (Fig. 49). The

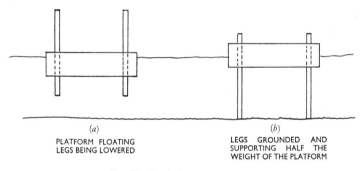

(a)
PLATFORM FLOATING
LEGS BEING LOWERED

(b)
LEGS GROUNDED AND
SUPPORTING HALF THE
WEIGHT OF THE PLATFORM

Fig. 49 Partly buoyant platform

weight of the pontoon platform was now shared. Part of it rested on the legs—just enough to keep the feet firmly on the bottom and prevent the staging overturning when struck by a ship. The rest of the pontoon's weight was carried by its own buoyancy in the water. The reason for this arrangement can best be understood by comparing what happens when a ship strikes the partly floating pontoon with the effect when the staging platform is raised clear of the water.

In Fig. 50 (a) and (b) the blow of the ship moves the platform, and since only the legs are in the water all the impulse energy of the ship is used in bending the legs. Clearly the legs have to be very strong and massive. In Fig. 50 (c) and (d), the same amount of energy has to be absorbed, but in this case, before the landing stage can move it has to push a lot of water out of the way

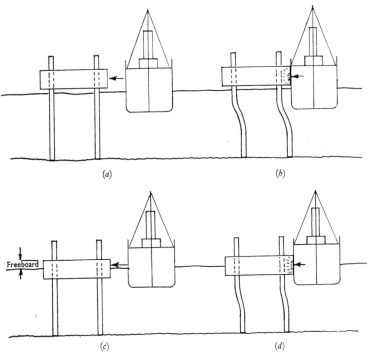

Fig. 50 Knees bend!

and so the water behind the pontoon takes a large share of the energy of the blow. This is clearly a better arrangement in every respect—for the purpose of berthing ships. But of course the freeboard must be maintained at a constant value or else the damping effect of the water will change. So the "leg winders" must be constantly at work keeping pace with the rise and fall of the tide. And so it was with Mulberry. But what has all this to do with us?

We want, remember, a rigid platform so that we can attach to it a dredging apparatus which will operate 200 feet down. And at that depth we must be able, by remote control from the surface, to bring the dredger head to bear on its task both forcefully and accurately. There is quite enough to attend to in this respect without having to inch the platform up and down with the tide as well. Furthermore, the advantage of the partly floating platform is working the opposite way for us, because wave action and tidal flow will have a much larger effect than if the staging were hoisted up clear of the water.

So we need the sort of thing shown in Fig. 50 (*a*) and (*b*) rather than (*c*) and (*d*). But it also has to be much more rigid, because it must stand steadier in deeper water than the Mulberry planners dreamed of.*

All this too has been done before. Drilling in the North Sea for oil and gas is a comparatively recent industry, but the equipment being used for it is much the same as has been used for many years in the Caribbean Sea and elsewhere. These oil-drilling marine platforms all have to provide steady rigid bases for the drilling machinery. They all use the same principle of prodding legs into the sea-bed until the platform is lifted clear of the wave tops. Cylindrical steel legs have been found suitable for this purpose, and the round shape lends itself to easy and quick operation by a special kind of hydraulic jack. It consists of a pair of steel collars, each of which can be expanded or contracted independently so as to release or grip the cylindrical leg. The lower collar of each jack assembly is fixed to the pontoon and the two collars can be closed together or separated by hydraulic rams. By cyclic operation of the correct sequence of gripping, releasing, and pumping, the leg can be slid smoothly up or down inside the jack (Fig. 51). And clearly if the leg has reached the sea-bed and jacking continues, the platform will ride up the leg. As the platforms get bigger and their weights exceed 300 tons or so per leg, the grip-release type of jack reaches the limit of its capacity. And for the very large platforms the leg movement is effected by a ratchet climbing up and down a steel ladder fixed to the leg.

Marine platforms using these leg-jacking systems are now working in very deep water. In some cases the depth is so great that four of the most massive legs are still not stiff enough and here the platforms are fitted with eight legs.

Now these drilling platforms are concerned only with drilling

---

*It should be emphasized here that the bending of the legs has been greatly exaggerated in Fig. 50, for the sake of explanation. In fact, the horizontal movement of a properly designed platform standing in 200 feet of water would range from a few inches up to possibly 2 feet and would rarely exceed the movement at the top of a tall brick chimney in a high wind.

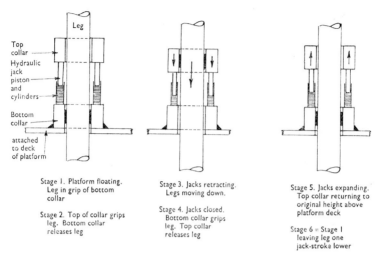

Top collar
Hydraulic jack piston and cylinders
Bottom collar
attached to deck of platform

Leg

Stage 1. Platform floating. Leg in grip of bottom collar

Stage 2. Top of collar grips leg. Bottom collar releases leg

Stage 3. Jacks retracting. Legs moving down.

Stage 4. Jacks closed. Bottom collar grips leg. Top collar releases leg

Stage 5. Jacks expanding. Top collar returning to original height above platform deck

Stage 6 = Stage 1 leaving leg one jack-stroke lower

Fig. 51   Jack the leg-puller

a deep hole vertically downwards.   This takes a long time, and when it is done the platform can be refloated in somewhat leisurely (though careful) fashion and moved to the next site.   A problem arises during the refloating which is not unduly worrying when the operation of moving is relatively infrequent and a delay in waiting for calm weather is a small proportion of the working period.   If, however, we are to use this sort of platform for supporting our Channel trench dredger this special problem

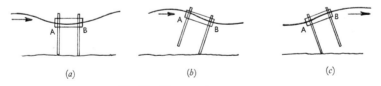

(a)

(b)

(c)

Fig. 52   The prancing pontoon

assumes entirely different importance, for our platform must be continually on the move.   The trouble is illustrated in Fig. 52 where a four-legged platform (*a*) is in the process of being floated (by raising the legs).   It is just about to become buoyant, that is, the feet are resting very lightly on the bottom—when along comes a wave (*b*). The depth of water at A increases and that at B decreases. The end A is suddenly buoyant, whilst at B the leg prods hard into the sea-bed. As the wave passes (*c*) the situation reverses. As further waves pass the whole contraption prances on the sea-bed like a scalded cat. Expensive-sounding creaks and groans will be heard at the aperture where the legs pass through the body. And if the distance between successive waves happens to be about twice the length of the platform the rocking motion will become resonant—and disaster is unavoidable.

Waiting for the sea to subside to a flat calm is a feasible solution where these platforms were first commonly used. But the Channel is rarely like a mill pond, and we cannot wait. Yet it seems to be courting disaster to make a move!

THE GIANT CRAB

And so the fight to outwit the sea goes on. Necessity is the mother of invention. The need to prevent our dredging rig prancing over the sea-bed like a crazy crab is no exception. Designers went into huddle after huddle and produced scheme after scheme. Finally, there emerged a design of platform which will do the job. Some of the details of this design cannot be revealed* but Fig. 53 (facing p. 161) is an artist's impression of the basic idea.

A great steel flat box A will be fitted with three pairs of legs B which can be jacked up or down to any required depth. When the dredger C is working, these six legs will stand on the sea-bed and the platform A will be raised clear of the highest waves. *It will never touch the water again until the job is finished.*

Housed within the belly of platform A is another platform D, longer and narrower than A, sliding in guides which are part of the outer structure. Platform D is fitted with four pairs of legs E which can also be raised or lowered at will. Four of these legs pass upwards through slots F in the outer platform A which

---

*This is not unreasonable. A number of groups of contracting companies, including the Author's own employers, are interested in the Channel Tunnel, and when a decision is finally made that it will be built there will be keen competition between these consortia to obtain the contract. They cannot therefore be expected to divulge all their secrets now.

permit the platform D and its legs to move a horizontal distance of 60 feet whilst A is standing still.

The inner platform D also carries the dredger head C which is supported by and moves with the crosshead G, which in turn slides (under control) on two of the legs E. All four motions of the cutter—rotating, swinging from side to side, benching downwards after each swing, and thrusting forward into the next vertical layer—are controlled from the platform. The swinging arm H on which the cutter head C is mounted houses the pump which draws water through the cutters to carry the excavated chalk up the inside of the central stack J. This stack is of course mounted on the inner platform D and passes through a further slot K in platform A so permitting the inner platform to slide unimpeded. The slurry is then pumped out to the end of one of the arms L and is discharged 120 feet from the platform. There are two of these arms so that whichever way the tide is running it can be co-opted into carrying the muck away from the trench.

The sequence in which the cutter head will advance into the sea-bed will be exactly as described on p. 152 and in Fig. 48. Each semi-circular sweep will gouge out a bench about 4 feet deep. The dredger head (shown enlarged in Fig. 54) will be lowered, with the cutter still turning, until it is embedded another 4 feet deep and will start its return sweep. This will be repeated, each sweep being a little shorter than the previous one so as to form the side slopes of the trench, until the trench bottom is reached. Then the dredger arm will be raised until the cutter is again at sea-bed level, the platform D (and everything attached to it) is advanced a distance of 8 feet and the cutter starts on the next series of sweeping cuts.

This can happen again and again, advancing the trench 8 feet each time until the platform D is brought to a halt by the legs E (Fig. 53) reaching the forward ends of the slots F. At this stage, the legs E are jacked down to the sea-bed, so that all fourteen legs are now supporting the double-platform structure—which is still clear of the waves. Then by careful manipulation of the jacking pressures the load is transferred from legs B to legs E, and legs B are raised clear of the bottom. The inner platform D is now supporting the outer platform A and its legs B, which are now slid forward about 60 feet. The next step is the reverse transfer of the load from inner legs E to outer legs B, still keeping the platform clear of the water. The legs E are once again at the rear ends of the slots F and everything is set to dredge another 60-foot length of trench.

There is a snag which Figs. 53 and 54 will make clear to the mechanically minded reader. If the operation proceeds exactly as described above, the two legs carrying the crosshead on which the dredger-head is mounted are supported only at platform level, high above the sea-bed. When therefore the rotating cutter is being forced into the chalk there is an enormous backward leverage on these two legs. Adding the stresses which might arise from slight swaying movements of the platform itself in heavy weather, could cause difficulty, especially if at that juncture the cutters are working in harder-than-average material.

In these circumstances it would be necessary to wind down the two legs supporting the crosshead so as to obtain a purchase on the sea-bed against which the dredger may be safely thrust. But this would involve raising and lowering these two legs each time the dredger had made an 8-foot step forward. The time required for this repeated double operation—although slight— would eat into the contingency time allowance (which is the difference between programmed dredging time and actual dredging time).

Modifications in the design of the crosshead are being considered. They will not only result in the elimination of time wasted in playing hopscotch with a pair of legs, but will also make easier the task of bringing up the dredger-head clear of the water surface for maintenance and the frequent changes of cutters which will be necessary.

Having ironed out these problems our fourteen-legged* monster will go striding across the Channel, with wet feet but a dry tummy, and with a gait we can reasonably call stilted.

TROUBLE ON THE WAY?

The marching colossus will not have things all its own way. Peculiarities of the sea-bed, the weather conditions, tidal currents,

---

*It is possible that when some current re-thinking is completed the number of legs can be reduced to twelve (6 + 6). It is immaterial to the argument here.

By courtesy of Lawrence Machine and Manufacturing Inc

Fig. 18 Alkirk Tunneler, and (inset) enlargement of roller showing tungsten-carbide inserts

L

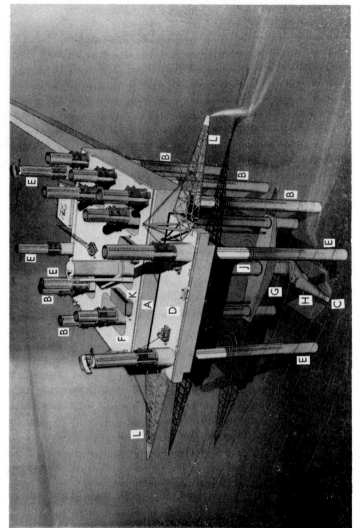

Fig. 53   The sea monster

ships of all nations, wrecks, and telegraph cables all present special demands which must be satisfied or appeased. The manner in which all these demands have to be met will—as usual—be a compromise, and would be largely responsible for deciding the route this type of tunnel would have to take.

Pathfinding

First it should be noted, in passing, that one of the main advantages claimed for the immersed-tube type of tunnel over the bored tunnel is not entirely obtainable in the Channel crossing. If the land inshore were reasonably low and level on both sides, and if the main transport networks to be connected were not already developed, then the lengths of the two types of tunnel would depend only on two factors: (a) the depth at which the shore line is crossed; and (b) the maximum permissible gradient.

Fig. 56   The deeper the longer?

Fig. 56 shows clearly the comparison between the necessary lengths of the two types of tunnel. This is, however, stating the advantage a little unfairly, because the cost per mile of construction is not the same for each type and it could be in certain circumstances that the longer length of the bored tunnel turns out to be cheaper to build than the shorter length of immersed tube. It is not yet possible to pronounce on relative costs.

In any case, the locations of the terminal areas where Tunnel traffic will interchange with national routes are already determined. This fact means that the Tunnel on the English side must run through several miles of the chalk cliffs before emerging behind Folkestone. So the only savings in length possible would arise from the slightly shorter approach tunnel on the French side and the siting of the submarine route some distance to the south-west of the line proposed for the bored tunnel.

It is in this latter respect that one of the main advantages of the immersed-tube tunnel is claimed. We have already seen how the route for the bored tunnel has been decided, and that it must follow a clearly defined path within very close limits.

L

The geological limitations are much kinder to the immersed tube proposal, for choice of its route is limited only by the need for the sea-bed material to be amenable to dredging to the necessary depth. Clearly, rock outcrops must be avoided. So must free-flowing sand or mud. Heavy clay too would be a nuisance and would probably require a different design of cutter-head. (Since the cutter-head will have to be changed frequently anyway, this should not matter very much).

There is, however, quite a wide band across the Channel, south-west of the Upper Chalk/Lower Chalk interface outcrop in which the dredger would work satisfactorily. And the route can be chosen anywhere within this band so as best to meet all the other problems which will arise.

One of the most difficult of these other problems concerns the maximum permissible gradient. It is a condition laid down by the railway operators that the gradient must nowhere exceed 1 in 100. But the Channel bed is far from flat and there are several areas to be negotiated where the bed slope exceeds 1 in 100. This means that for short distances the trench will have to be dug somewhat deeper than the average, so as to carry the route through the humps rather in the manner that a land railway line traverses a shallow hump in a cutting. And the dredging equipment has been designed to get down to 70 feet below the sea-bed when necessary.

There are many wrecks lying on the Channel bed, and it was for a long time believed that a number of them would have to be moved to clear a path for the walking platform. This would be an extremely difficult and expensive task, but persistence has been rewarded by the discovery of one or two straight lines across the Channel which tread daintily between all these wrecks and it now seems likely that not even the slightest deviation from a straight line would be required. And so one more nightmare has been dispelled.

Other possible entanglements have to be treated rather differently. Unlike wrecks which could be removed or sidestepped, telegraph cables cannot be avoided and must not be taken away. This problem has met its Waterloo. It is a tribute to international co-operation (British-French-German-Italian) that discussion has already demonstrated the prospect of satisfactory arrangements being agreed. Some of the cables would be temporarily diverted before the tunnel work started. In other cases, new cables would be laid over a completed section of the tunnel and connected up before the works reached the existing lines. The old lines would then be removed.

Ships that pass

The Straits of Dover is one of the busiest shipping channels in the world and the daily traffic can amount to 200 ships. Many of the North Sea ports, but chiefly those in the Thames, can be entered only at high tide, so the ships tend to come in surges and the average hourly traffic flow may at times be greatly exceeded. Furthermore, the Varne Bank in the middle of the Channel further concentrates the traffic into two main channels.

Visibility is down to 5 miles on about 100 days in the year, and for roughly 25 days in the year fog makes navigation hazardous, even in unobstructed waterways.

For all these reasons there will clearly be a major task in maintaining an efficient safety and warning system. Ships and platform will have to be protected from each other. Subject to agreement with Trinity House a system has been devised, conforming with "The Convention of the Continental Shelf" (1st United Nations Conference on the Law of the Sea) Article 5.3. This article refers to a safety zone of 500 metres radius, which may extend around installations erected to explore or exploit the sea-bed. So the walking platform and all its auxiliaries would operate within a circle one kilometre in diameter.

The platform would of course be fitted with a radar control centre which would constantly plot the positions of all ships approaching the vicinity of the safety area. Lightships and light buoys would surround the works and would move along with them. Ample fog signals would be required in times of bad visibility.

A powerful tug, equipped for communication in the international language of the sea would be constantly on stand-by for warning and possibly assisting any ship observed to be in difficulty or danger. And of course all maritime authorities would be kept constantly informed of the day-to-day position of the obstruction.

Wind and Wave

Although the walking platform has been designed to stand firmly on the sea-bed in all conditions of wind, wave, and tide, it is not feasible to make it so rigid that the deck would be absolutely still in the worst conditions. Some movement is inevitable and it remains now to balance the amount of movement which can be permitted, whilst the dredger is still working, against the frequency of weather conditions which could cause a stoppage. In drawing up this balance sheet, we must have regard to the number of days in each year on which work must carry on if the job is to be completed in the programmed time.

The height of waves and their frequency combine to be the sole threat to continuous working of the dredger-carrying platform. Although perfectly safe and stable, it is always possible to put all fourteen legs down on the sea-bed, but this would of course hold up the dredging work.

There is little reliable information of wave heights in the Channel (or anywhere else for that matter), because there is no way of recording except by visual impressions. And it is well known that two mariners on the same ship, each saying "the waves were . . . feet high" can differ by 100 per cent or more.*

However, waves are caused by wind and a great deal is known about wind velocities, which have been assiduously and accurately recorded over a number of years. Furthermore, after making due allowance for "fetch,"† the proximity of shoals and coasts which can "reflect" waves, the height of the resulting waves can be calculated fairly accurately.

Basing such calculations on the windiest of the past 15 years,

---

*In fairness to a particular group of dedicated men, it should be stated here that the crews of lightships off the Kent coast have had a great deal of experience in the visual estimation of wave heights.

The crew of a German light vessel, captains of cross-Channel steamers, and the Dover Harbour Engineer and Harbourmaster have also contributed carefully considered opinions based on long acquaintance with the enemy. Their averaged judgements have shown remarkable conformity with other methods of wave-height estimation considered less subject to human error. Their observations were made some distance away from the narrowest neck of water which the Channel Tunnel must cross, but have been most useful.

†"Fetch" is the distance to the nearest shore line measured in a straight line in the direction from which the wind is blowing.

it has been discovered that dredging can be continued on a sufficient number of days to complete the programme with plenty of
time to spare.

DIRECTION FINDING

The first directional problem is a very general one. The
marine operation could start at the French coast and end at the
English coast; or it could start on the Kent shore and end in
France; or it could work simultaneously from both sides and
join in the middle.* Each of the three possible sequences
present different problems of linking up the submarine tunnel
with the landward tunnels, but there is also a great deal that is
common to them. The Author's personal preference is for the
scheme which would start at the French coast and cross the
Channel in a continuous smooth operation, joining up with the
landward tunnel at the English coast line. For this reason, and
to avoid being repetitious, the descriptions which follow are
confined to that sequence.

When the dredging platform first starts its north-westerly
route march from coast to coast it will not be difficult to point
its nose in the right direction, but every time it takes a stride,
wind and water pressures may cause slight deviations from the
true line as the weight is transferred from the inner to the outer
legs, and *vice versa*. So after every movement is completed,
the exact position of the platform will have to be checked and if
there is any deviation from the true line, a suitable correction
can be made in the next stride forward.

Positional checks can be made by optical means during the
early part of the journey, but as the shore line recedes, visibility
will worsen, and we cannot wait for the weather to clear if the
conditions are otherwise propitious for getting on with the job.

So radar slave stations will be set up on shore and by means
of a radar master station on the platform intersecting bearings
can be taken simultaneously to give positional check. Now the
slightest error in these bearings could result in an inaccuracy of

---

*The fourth possibility of starting in the middle and working both ways
to the coasts presents so many difficulties, such as accurate location of starting
point and access to the tunnel interior during construction, that it has not
been considered even remotely possible.

some inches either side of the true line when the platform is farthest from the coast (i.e., in mid-Channel). However, for a number of other reasons the bottom of the trench will be dug a few feet wider than the bottom of the prefabricated tunnel which is to lie in it. So, if the trench alignment does deviate a foot or so either way, the tunnel units can still be laid in a straight line.

CHAPTER FOURTEEN

Piecemeal tunnel making

which is another way of defining the prefabrication of the individual hollow units, which, when floated to position, sunk, and joined, will form a continuous submarine tunnel

WHEN A LINING IS NOT A LINING

WE HAVE already seen in Chapter 10 that a tunnel bored through the Lower Chalk would *have* to be lined, and that it would probably be lined with concrete. Chapter 6 showed how a waterproof lining could be made of prefabricated concrete blocks.

The modern trend for prefabrication in any sort of construction is for the individual units to be made as large as possible, with two provisos: first that large numbers all of one size and shape are required; and secondly that one must be able to transport them from where they are made to where they have to be installed. Both of these provisos are significant when comparing bored tunnel with immersed-tube tunnel. The dimensions of the precast segments used for lining a bored tunnel would be measured in *feet* because they would have to be transported from casting yard, lowered down a shaft, turn the corner from shaft to tunnel, then travel through a tunnel already cluttered up with equipment of all sorts. When all joined together, these segments will form a watertight tube in their own right. Why bother to make a great hole in the rock to accommodate them? Why not just lay this "lining" on the sea-bed? Indeed, when is a lining not a lining?

It becomes . . . ?

The answer is, of course, twofold. First, the pressure of the water seeping through the rock into the bored tunnel will usually be less than the pressure of 200 feet depth of "solid" water. So, except in the case of the tunnel borers meeting an unexpected fault or infilled valley (see pp. 83-87), the joints between their lining segments are not quite so critical. Furthermore, setting the segments into position and sealing the joints can be done in dry conditions in a well lighted tunnel. Joining the sections of an immersed-tube tunnel is much more difficult.

On the other hand, the prefabricated units of an immersed tube can be 500 feet long and the number of joints required will be correspondingly less. Provided that a satisfactory temporary watertightness can be achieved when the sections are first laid down, finishing the job to any required standard of safety can, in this case too, be done in the dry, from inside a well lighted tunnel.

But if we raise the tunnel lining out of the deep rock and lay it in the sea-bed we raise with it a whole host of new problems in the design office. Some of these are well known to shipbuilders, for they concern the very complicated stresses which are imposed on floating shells by towing and wave action. Stability problems too are no longer a headache to naval architects, who know all about rolling and pitching motions, and the ease with which a badly designed hull can turn turtle.

On the other hand, a ship is designed not only to float but to stay afloat. Our tunnel hulls must float at first, but must sink when we want them to, and must remain sunk. They must be watertight and pressure resistant at top, bottom, and sides.

And so we come to the problem of the cross-sectional shape.

A Study of Form

There have been many different shapes used for immersed-tube tunnels. But it should not be thought that engineers cannot make up their minds which is the best. Type and quantity of traffic generally will decide how wide the tunnel is to be inside. Water depth above the tunnel will then dictate the best shape which will accommodate that width economically.

Some immersed-tube tunnels have been built with a rectangular cross-section, but none of these provides a navigation depth of more than 50 feet. The Coentunnel which is under construction in Amsterdam, will have 72 feet of water over it when completed. So massive is the construction of the units for this tunnel that it seems unlikely that rectangular sections could be used economically for water much deeper than 72 feet.

We have already seen the greatly superior strength of circular cross-sections and the majority of the American immersed-tube tunnels have cross-sections which approximate to the circle.

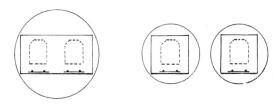

Fig. 57   One tunnel or two?

But it should be noted that the depth of a circular tunnel which is to provide sufficient width for twin tracks is greater than is required for two tunnels carrying one track in each direction (Fig. 57). In the case of the Channel Tunnel this raises five major points:—

(a)   The arch-strength of the smaller tunnels is much greater, so their concrete walls need not be as thick as that of the single large tunnel. Furthermore the hollow space inside the single bore is much larger than the combined hollow spaces in the twin bore. This would make it comparatively much more buoyant and a great deal more concrete than that required for its structural strength would have to be put into it to *hold it down* in the trench.

(b)   The single large tunnel would require a much deeper trench and the amount of dredging required would be greater than required for the housing of the pair of smaller single-track tunnels.

(c)   The smaller-diameter tunnels would have to be prefabricated in shorter lengths so as to be rigid enough for launching and towing.

(d) Two smaller tunnels would almost double the work of making and laying the units, and the plant requirements would likewise be approximately doubled.

(e) It would be almost impossible to arrange for crossovers and access between the two small tunnels.

Now (a) and (b) operate in favour of the two smaller tunnels; (c) and (d) operate against them; (e) is the most powerful argument of all against separate one-track tunnels, for it is almost unthinkable to have two tunnels running side by side for more than twenty miles without access from one to the other. Should there be a hold-up in one of them—or even worse, an accident— the consequences are easily imagined.

How then are we to compromise between these warring factors? The solution is simple in conception, although it raises design problems of great complexity when the stresses due to water pressure are minutely analysed. Concrete has great strength in compression but practically none in tension. Wherever any appreciable tension occurs in concrete, it will crack, and this would not do at all under 200 feet of water! Now a purely circular tunnel, as we have seen, is a continuous arch and only compressive stresses can occur in it. As soon as we depart from the truly circular section, this stress symmetry is upset. In the language of structural engineering, bending moments arise. And one of the components of the bending moment is tension. It must be avoided.

Fig. 58 shows diagrammatically how the great strength of the circular section can be used without involving too deep a trench, and at the same time allowing for frequent access connexions between the two bores.

This cross-section has many advantages which neither the large single circle nor the pair of smaller circles can offer. Chief of these is the fact that any change in requirements of the railway operators can be allowed for right up to the last moment before construction commences, with the minimum of extra cost. For example, if instead of the two walkways it is decided that a central passageway is required throughout the length of the tunnel, then the central wall can be widened to accommodate it (Fig. 59).

Or it may even be decided at a later stage that a third railway

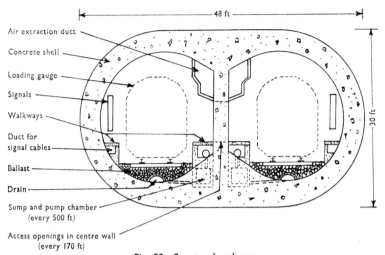

Air extraction duct

Concrete shell

Loading gauge

Signals

Walkways

Duct for
signal cables

Ballast

Drain

Sump and pump chamber
(every 500 ft)

Access openings in centre wall
(every 170 ft)

48 ft

30 ft

Fig. 58   Spectacular shape

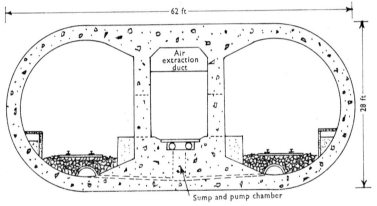

62 ft

28 ft

Air
extraction
duct

Sump and pump chamber

Fig. 59   Three tunnels?

track would be desirable to cope with "tidal" traffic (in the same way that two of the four lanes of Chelsea Bridge in London are reversed to cope with the morning and evening rush-hour motor traffic).

There are many possible uses of a third passage, and the cost of installing it would be a comparatively minor addition to the total cost.

THE TUNNEL FACTORY

The prefabrication of the concrete bits and pieces which go to make up a land-based structure, such as an office building, a road bridge, or a dock wall, is a well established practice. The smaller items, such as road kerbs, paving stones, and window sills can be churned out in thousands inside a factory building. And since concrete, like bacon, has to be cured before it can be used, these factories are often supplied with steam ovens, called autoclaves, to hasten the curing process which may, in the open air take days, weeks, or even months, according to the strength standards required.

Larger items, such as bridge beams which can be more than a hundred feet long and weigh upwards of a hundred tons, are not so easily slung around, as they are usually "cast" out in the open in what is called a "casting yard." Here the moulds are carefully arranged so that after an initial setting period the shutters can be stripped off the just-hard concrete and set up again in the next bay, leaving the "green" concrete to cure. There is no great difficulty in all this, but when the great hunks of cured concrete have to be taken from their casting beds to where they are to be used, problems of transport arise. If the casting yard is very near to the building site, these large units can be jacked up on to rollers or bogeys and hauled into place. But it is often necessary to use the public highways. Each of these types of movement lays a restriction on the maximum size of structure which can be prefabricated.

But in the case of prefabricated lengths of tunnel tubing, which can be floated from where they are built to where they are wanted, the limit to size is imposed mainly by the capabilities of the equipments which are to tow them (under control) and to control them while they are being sunk into the trench. Of the thirty or so tunnels which have been built in this fashion, the great majority have used a unit length of about 300 feet. This has resulted from a combination of many circumstances:—

(a) Economic maximum size of area which can be set aside as a casting yard.
(b) Maximum power of available tugs.
(c) Prevailing wave-lengths in the stretch of water to be negotiated.

(d) Limitations of the equipment used for lowering the units.

(e) Problems of thermal expansion and contraction both during building and after laying.

And so on.

In the case of the Channel Tunnel, however, the job is so large that it would become economical to design special equipment rather than rely on what is already available. Furthermore, owing to the greater water pressures the tunnel will have to withstand, the cross-section of the tunnel will be much stronger than those of its forerunners. This makes for greater stiffness and longer lengths can be used without fear of breaking their backs in a long swell when being towed. It is probable that a length of 500 feet would be adopted for each prefabricated tunnel unit.

SLIPWAY OR DRY DOCK ?

The sections will of course have to be built on dry land, so there remains the problem of getting them into the water. There are two ways of doing this. Either the tunnel shell can be built on a slipway, like a ship, and launched. Or it can be built in a dry dock below water-level and floated out when ready.

Slipways

The slipway method has been used in the United States, where the usual first step is to build a large steel tube surrounded by an even larger steel tube. Blanking-off plates are built across the open ends and enough concrete is placed in the bottom of the annular space between the tubes to ensure that they float in the right attitude when launched. After launching, the unfinished tunnel unit is towed to a wet dock where the remainder of the annulus is almost filled with concrete. Enough space is left unfilled to ensure that the unit will remain afloat and stable until it is about to be lowered. This method allows the slipway to be used again and again in quick succession without having to wait long periods for the concrete to cure. Furthermore, it need be only a comparatively light structure, for the double steel tube weighs only a few hundred tons without its concrete filling.

Dry docks

The Dutch, who are the second most prolific builders of immersed-tube tunnels prefer the dry-dock method. In many ways the problems they have to contend with are similar to those which would confront the Channel Tunnel tube makers; for although the Dutch and the French (whose share in the Channel project might well include the prefabrication) have plenty of dry docks big enough for the job, they are far from the site of the Tunnel. Furthermore, the withdrawal of a number of dry docks for several years from their proper purpose of maintaining a nation's maritime fleet would not be acceptable.

The Dutch method is to dig a large pit near the water's edge, leaving a narrow neck of land to keep out the flood. The excavated area is usually large enough to accommodate several units being constructed at the same time.

Seepage water has to be excluded as far as possible and the dock area is usually isolated from its surroundings by a wall of interlocking sheet-piles (a "cut-off" wall). These are driven down to such a depth that the water outside has to percolate a very long way in order to invade the dry dock; the quantity which does get through is easily pumped out through narrow wells just inside the sheet-piles. (This is known as "well-point dewatering").

Now there is a nearly dry floor on which a concrete slab base is laid to support the tunnel units as they are built and the plant which is going to build them.

But once this floor is laid, another problem arises, which is well known in dock engineering. Although our sheet-pile wall has excluded seepage water sufficiently to prevent the pit flooding and to enable the excavation and subsequent floor-concreting to proceed, there is still a seepage. This percolating water will collect under the concrete floor and will eventually build up a pressure equal to the head h in Fig. 60. This is called the "uplift" pressure and could heave up the dock floor if not dealt with. Over part of the area the uplift pressure can be relieved by putting "weepholes" through the concrete. The water can then flow into the dock and be pumped away. But the tunnel units will cover large areas and there can be no such relief holes beneath them. So the floor has to be made heavy enough to resist the uplift. This means a lot of concrete, and up goes the cost.

When the tunnel sections are ready for floating out, the dock is flooded; a hole is made in the embankment separating it from the open water, and off they go to their rendezvous with the sinking crew.

If further units are to be built in the same dock (and this would certainly be the case many times over if the Channel Tunnel sections were to be built in a dry dock) the hole in the embankment is squared up and plugged with a caisson-type gate. This is a large steel or concrete box with buoyancy chambers

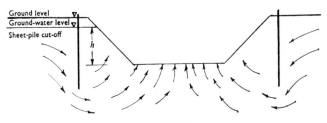

Fig. 60   Uplift head

which can be flooded or pumped out at will, to permit dewatering of the dock and subsequent exit of more tunnel units.

Which method would be used for the Channel Tunnel units? This will be a very difficult decision to make for there are many arguments pulling both ways. Of these, two can be singled out for discussion in some detail.

Pro slip

A very much larger number of units (more than 250) would be required than for any other tunnel yet built by the immersed-tube method. The tubular units which have, up to now, been built in a dry dock have been brought to a more advanced state of completion before floating than those built on a slipway. Each unit has taken several months to construct. But laying the Channel Tunnel units on the sea-bed will be done every few days during the summer season. This means two things.

There must be a large number of the tunnel sections completed before the laying process starts, and so there will have to be a long period of storage for the first-built units; secondly, since the building of tunnel units must not only get well ahead of laying them in the trench but must keep well ahead, there would have to be a dry-dock area large enough for eight or more units to be under construction at the same time. This is an enormous land requirement, and since storage space between construction and the laying will have to be provided *anyway* it seems, on the basis of what has been done before, that the slipway method has an overwhelming advantage.

Pro dock

On the other hand there is a very big difference between the type of structure which the Americans have built partly on slipway and partly in wet basin and the type of structure likely to be used for the Channel Tunnel units. In the first place, the purely circular sections of steelwork built on a slipway and then launched before concreting have to be designed for three entirely different conditions of stress:—

(a) Stresses in the steel shell, due to its own weight, when resting on the slipway and when raised on its carriages ready for launching.

(b) The range of stress conditions during launching, when the end entering the water first becomes buoyant and lifts, so throwing all the remaining weight on the top carriage.

(c) The stresses caused by waves during floating and towing. (The movement of waves along the length of the unit can cause considerable uplift forces to traverse every part of the section).

The conditions of stress when the tunnel is laid on the sea-bed are omitted from this group of design considerations, because we have not yet reached the stage where all the concrete has been installed. Nevertheless the conditions are severe enough to warrant a very stiff construction, using much more steel than would be required if they did not exist. Steel is a much more costly building material than concrete, and so when the total number of prefabricated units jumps from a few to a few hundred, this extra cost becomes much more important.

Fig. 54   The chalk-eater

By courtesy of Mr. J. Weaver of C. & C.A.

Fig. 55   Below the Maas

Fig. 61　Platform 2

The units proposed for the Channel Tunnel are intended to be dependent for their strength entirely on concrete. So any permanent steel used in their construction can be considered an unnecessary expense. However, the casting of concrete requires shuttering and the steel shell which is to perform this function would be the first item of construction. For economy it would be of minimum thickness. It would not even have the advantage of pure circular form, and it would certainly collapse under the stresses of launching.

This means that the units would have to be *completed* on the slipway. And more problems arise. First, the slipway will be occupied for the same length of time as would a dry dock, and so there would have to be more of them—with the attendant additional space requirements. Secondly, the slipway would have to support a much greater maximum weight and the foundations will be correspondingly more expensive.

So what ?

No decision can be made until a very careful cost analysis has been completed. The time is not yet ripe for this, since conditions such as land availability and the relative costs of steel and concrete may change before the work can start.

CHAPTER FIFTEEN

At sea

which covers a whole host of operations from the launching of the units to the time when the tunnel is really a tunnel

TO FLOAT OR NOT TO FLOAT?

RISKING THE tedium of repetition, it is again emphasized that the tunnel units, when built, must float. This is to say they must have positive buoyancy. Later they must sink and stay sunk. So they must at some stage have their positive buoyancy changed to negative buoyancy. There are two quite different ways in which this can be done, whether the units are built in dry dock or on a slipway.

In the first method, the concreting of the top can be left incomplete so that when the unit is first launched from the casting yard it will float with a few hundred tons of positive buoyancy. In that condition (completely watertight of course) it will be stored until wanted, then towed out to the position where it is to be sunk. Here, more concrete will be placed on top, positioning each bucketful in a carefully calculated sequence so that the structure remains stable and level. Before it actually begins to sink, powerful tackles will be attached so that the lowering can be done under complete control. Then the final few loads of concrete will be placed until the tension in the tackles shows that the positive buoyancy has changed to negative buoyancy. Then comes the period of greatest concentration, for when the great concrete tube disappears sedately beneath the waves on the start of its long downward journey, the difficulties of control assume a new dimension. Sensitive hands on the winch levers, accurate instrumentation, complex systems of rapid communication between operators and the central controller, the ability to make quick and correct decision, all dovetail together to land the concrete monster on the sea-bed within very few inches of its correct position.

The second method of ensuring the required change of buoyancy from positive to negative is quite different. In this case the concreting is completed before floating the unit. In this condition of course it cannot be launched, because it is now the weight it should be when laid in the trench. How do we get it there? Before we put the unit in the water for the first time we must attach pontoons to the top or sides. (Most likely the top, for this will simplify the problem of recovering the pontoons and will reduce the overall width of the combination and so the space required for manoeuvering). The pontoons will probably be long steel cylinders, with a large number of separate compartments which can be filled with water or pumped out. They will be attached to the tunnel section in such a way that the fastenings can be released by remote control. The rest is now obvious, for the unit, which, when completed will have a negative buoyancy of about 200 tons, can be made to float or sink at will.

But which is the better way? The first method requires that concrete mixing plant, large quantities of concrete-making materials, and all the other equipment which goes with concreting operations, have to be available when wanted at the site of the sinking of each unit.

On the other hand, the pontoons are an additional and expensive item, and their installation will add to the time of occupation of slipway or dry-dock. The "towing weight" of the units will be much greater and handling them at sea will be correspondingly more difficult.

All these points, and many other minor ones, will have to be examined in detail before an overall cost comparison can be made. And even if one method turns out to be slightly cheaper, safety considerations may turn the tables.

PLATFORM 2

We have now got our prefabricated tunnel unit to the position where it is to be lowered into its trench. And we have glibly talked of lowering it by tackle. But what holds the tackle at sea-level?

For most of the immersed-tube tunnels already built, floating craft have been sufficient. But these tunnels were laid where the surface conditions were flat calm, or where surface disturbance was so infrequent that delays caused by "waiting for the weather" were insignificant in the overall contract time. The Channel, however, is a different kettle of fish (no pun intended). Conditions calm enough for operation from floating craft are so rare that such a method cannot be considered even remotely possible.

This was, of course, one of the problems we had with the dredging part of the project, and Chapter 13 shows how we solved it.

So we need another walking platform. It will be very similar in design to the dredging platform, and will "walk" in exactly the same way. Fig. 61 (facing p. 177) shows how similar it can be. In this photograph, a tunnel section with its pontoons flooded is being lowered beneath the belly of the platform. The end of the previously laid section can be seen just to the right of the second outer leg. At the top right-hand corner, the units have been covered with backfill material. The ship is not, of course, resting on the tunnel, but is moored alongside the platform. A crane is "grabbing" sand and gravel from the ship's holds to replenish the bunkers which can be seen on the platform deck. The surface of the sea is not clearly shown but the water-level is indicated by the top of the dark shading on the platform legs.

Screeding

This platform can do an extra job which has as yet been only briefly mentioned. It should be remembered that the tunnel units must lie on a flat level floor. Their weight must be distributed evenly to prevent differential settlement and unacceptable stresses in the concrete structure. But the cutter-suction dredger cannot leave a surface as nicely level as we want it. So a layer of loose material (a "screed") must be placed on the trench bottom. And the leading end of our platform No. 2 can be fitted with an attachment which will do this. The general idea is similar to the method used for laying the surface of a road. A pile of the screed material is dumped in the middle of the trench floor and is spread to each side by an Archimedean screw (a long blade wound spirally round a spindle).

This screeding could equally well be done from the rear end

of the dredging platform. There will, however, be times when the dredging will get some way ahead (perhaps half a mile) of the tube laying. It is considered wise to lay the screed as late as possible, so that there is no chance of the level surface being disturbed.

Reception

Screeding done, we are ready to receive the tube which is next to go down. The work will be phased so that the tunnel unit with its escort of tugs arrives at exactly the right time. The programme allows for the unit to be warped carefully into position beneath the platform, the lowering and control wires to be attached, and lowering to commence about half an hour before slack water. (This can be at either high or low tide where the water is deep enough, but where the operations are near the coast it may be only at high water that the last one or two tubes can be floated into the bay beneath the platform).

GOING DOWN

The lowering must be completed before tidal currents begin to flow again after the slack-water period. This is clearly necessary, for when the tunnel unit is hanging nearly 200 feet down, any appreciable current would swing it many feet out of position. The tackles will be mounted on slides which can move a small distance (6 feet or so) each way *across* the platform. This will enable the position of the unit during lowering to be corrected for any inaccuracy in the position of the platform itself. But such adjustment could not account for the movement of the unit resulting from swift water currents.

It is easy to say that at the moment of high or low tide, and for a little time each side, there is no tidal current. But this is altogether too theoretical; it just doesn't happen that way. A moment's thought will show the unlikelihood of a great body of water flowing up the Channel, slowing down, stopping, and then flowing back again. It is more likely that some layers of water will reverse flow and others will lag behind, so there will be a short period when water is flowing in both directions past the suspension cables and the platform legs. And the current speed will be different at every depth.

So now it is necessary to define more accurately what we mean by "slack water"; it is in fact the maximum current velocity which can be tolerated during the trickier parts of the tube-laying operation. The period during which the current velocity is equal to or less than this maximum varies with the incidence of Spring and Neap tides, which in turn vary according to the relative positions of the Sun and Moon and their consequent pulls upon the Earth. At Spring-tide periods they pull together and the tidal range in the Channel is maximum. During Neap tides they pull in different directions and the tidal range is less. The final link in the chain of causation is that the length of the slack-water period depends on the tidal range.

Wind and wave

Having taken care of the tide-flow problem, we are now faced with more difficult—and less predictable—weapons of nature. Both wind and waves will cause slight lateral movements of the platform deck. It seems obvious that if the deck moves then so will anything suspended from it. But this is not necessarily so. If the wind is light and the water merely choppy, the deck movements will be small and rapid. On the other hand, the tunnel unit is very massive and when it is deeply submerged

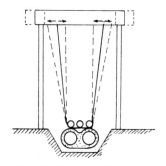

Fig. 62   Pendulum in reverse

its movement can only be very slow. The result is that it tends to remain stationary in a neutral position whilst the cables from which it hangs move comparatively quickly either side of their central position (Fig. 62). The reader can easily demonstrate this for himself by hanging a heavy weight on a long string then moving the hand holding the string rapidly from left to right. He will see that the weight will remain almost stationary.

As the wind force increases, waves carry more energy and the buffeting of the platform legs creates larger movements. At the same time the wave-lengths increase and the platform movements become slower. If the lateral oscillation of the platform becomes so slow that its "period" approaches the natural period of the tunnel unit then resonance sets in and a few inches periodic movement of the suspenders could soon create a swing of many feet in the suspended unit.

Tunnel laying would not be possible in these conditions.

Nevertheless, analysis of weather records shows that even if the worst recorded years are repeated in succession during the 3- or 4-year period required for laying a prefabricated Channel Tunnel, there would still be enough "good" days to get the job done—with time to spare.

JOINTS

When the tunnel unit is resting safe and level on its bed at the bottom of the trench, a short sigh of relief can be permitted. But there is still much tricky work to do. Because of the difficulties we have just discussed it is unlikely that the newly laid unit will be touching its predecessor. Indeed, because of the slight uncontrollable swinging movement it will have been deliberately put down in such a way that there will be a few feet clearance. Only at the last moment before grounding, will the suspended unit be swung to within an inch or two of the previously laid unit.

Getting close

When grounded, the situation will be as shown diagrammatically in Fig. 63. A is the newly laid unit. B, C, and D are the

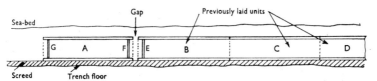

Fig. 63 Ready for joining up

previously laid tunnel sections. There is an inch or two of space between A and B. Letters E, F, and G indicate the diaphragms which keep the water out. Sea-water is trapped between diaphragms E and F, and it is worth remembering that there is water pressure all over the place; particularly we should note the pressures shown in Fig. 64, for the pressures on the diaphragms soon become very important.

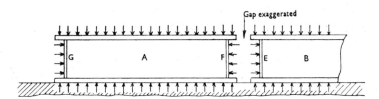

Fig. 64   Water, water, everywhere!

Clearly, when we close the gap, it will not be sufficient to have concrete meeting concrete; this will certainly not be water-tight. We must insert a jointing material which will have to fulfil a very exacting specification:—

1. It must be absolutely impervious to water.
2. It must be compressible so that it will properly bed into the concrete faces.
3. It must withstand great pressure without collapsing.
4. It must not deteriorate during long immersion in sea-water.

Natural rubber and artificial rubber of the chloroprene type are the only materials which match up to all these requirements.* Considerable experience has already been gained in the use of rubber gaskets for the joints between immersed-tube tunnel sections.   The most modern of these is the one used by the Dutch in their underwater tunnels at Rotterdam and Amsterdam.   It

---

*The Dutch have made tests on the rubber and neoprene of which their joints are made.   They subjected prototype gaskets to the conditions to which they will be exposed on both inside and outside, and artificially accelerated the effects of these conditions to such an extent that tests were equivalent to several hundreds of years immersion.   They are satisfied that by the time the rubber deteriorates, the tunnels will no longer be required.

In any case, when everything has settled down (see p. 000), a layer of concrete can be placed over the outside of the joint to protect the rubber from direct contact with sea-water.

consists of a solid ring of rubber having a cross-section similar to that shown in Fig. 65. Part of the newly laid tunnel unit is shown in section at A. The gasket was fixed to the unit B before it was launched. In the position shown, the unit A is about to be closed up to B. This can be done in several ways.

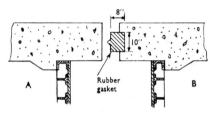

Fig. 65   Getting closer

In the case of the Channel Tunnel it is probable that a modification of the method used for the Deas Island Tunnel will be adopted. Here, a pair of giant hooks fixed to unit B were engaged in equally giant sockets built in to unit A. The hooks were then pulled to the right by remotely controlled hydraulic jacks until the concrete of unit A made contact with unit B.*

Getting closer

As soon as this contact is made and the rubber begins to compress, a new problem arises. For as soon as the whole periphery of the joint is closed sufficiently tightly to prevent water flowing in or out we have a temporarily dangerous situation. For we have enclosed between the diaphragms of units A and B (Fig. 64) a volume of water at high pressure—the same pressure as exists all round the outside of the tunnel. If we now squeeze the rubber ring any further we shall be trying to reduce this volume. But water is incompressible and the result would be an enormous increase of pressure in the enclosed water and either a diaphragm would burst to relieve it or the rubber ring

---

*This will not require as much force as may be thought, because although the tunnel unit will have a weight in air of about 20,000 tons, its weight in water will be only a fraction of this and can be lightened as required by partly blowing the pontoons which have not been removed. It will therefore require a force of something less than 100 tons to drag it the necessary few inches along the screed bed, plus a little extra to start compressing the rubber.

would blow out. Either would be disastrous. So a small duct ("bleed pipe") will be built into the end of unit B, which, by means of a valve, will allow a small, carefully controlled quantity of water to leak from the space between the diaphragms into tunnel unit B.

This valve will have a double purpose. First, it can be set to open automatically at a slightly higher pressure than that due to the depth of water above the tunnel. So that the compressed water between the diaphragms can relieve itself in just sufficient quantity to maintain its pressure constant. It is important that this pressure should not fall too low, as we shall see.

The second function of the valve will be useful later, for when the joining of the units has been completed and the space between the diaphragms is eventually pumped dry, the valve can be opened manually, and left open. It will then show if the jointing the gasket is in fact watertight, for if it is not, sea-water will fill the space again and weep through the valve into B, and we shall know that it is not yet safe to remove the diaphragms.

But we are running ahead too fast. Let us return to the point where the rubber joint has just been closed. Fig. 64 can now be modified to Fig. 66, which shows that the horizontal pressure

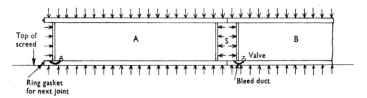

Fig. 66 Contact!

in the space S pushing the tunnel unit A to the left is the same as the pressure at the other end which is pushing it to the right. So the only force trying to close the joint together is the pull in the hydraulically operated hooks. If now we let a little more water through the bleed valve and so reduce the pressure in space S, the pressure of the sea-water at the left-hand end will push the unit A to the right and compress the rubber gasket even tighter (. . . "watertighter"?). And it seems that the water pressures which have so far been so troublesome have at last decided to be helpful!

Unfortunately this is only partly true. It is just fine where the water depth above the tunnel is not too great, but as we wade deeper we must think again. If we are working in 100 feet depth and let all the water out of the space S, then the horizontal force of the water on the outer end of unit A will be of the order of 5,000 tons. And all this will be acting on one rubber ring, which has a bearing area of less than 100 square feet. The rubber would give up the ghost and disintegrate very smartly. And at 200 feet depth . . .!

There are several ways of dealing with this disappointment. First, we could use harder types of rubber for the greater depths, as the Dutch are doing in the Rotterdam Metro tunnel (Fig. 55). But there is a limit to the hardness of rubber which will fulfill the

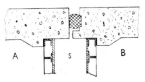

Fig. 67   The squeeze limit

other specifications for our gasket material; and this limit would be exceeded in the deepest parts of the Channel.

Secondly, we could insert concrete stops so that the rubber could be compressed so far but no farther. (Fig. 67 shows the

Flat jack before pumping   Flat jack pressurized

Fig. 68   Flat jack

idea). But this complicates the prefabrication of the tubes, for each depth of water would require a different length of concrete buffer.

Thirdly, a method somewhat similar to that in use by the Dutch in the IJ Tunnel in Amsterdam, is to place "flat jacks" in the joint so that when the rubber ring has been compressed as much as it will stand, the jacks will prevent the tunnel units moving any closer together. ("Flat jacks" (Fig. 68) are disc-shaped capsules of thin metal: they are filled with oil which can be pumped up to any desired pressure.) When additional tunnel units have been laid and no more "closing" movement is likely, the jacks can be removed and the spaces they occupied filled with concrete.

The method most likely to be used for Channel Tunnel joints is illustrated in Fig. 69, which is not entirely self-explanatory.

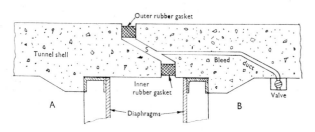

Fig. 69 Bleeding the joint

First we see that a taper is incorporated in the periphery of each tunnel unit. This allows for the difficulty of lowering tunnel unit A into exactly the right position for mating up with the already laid unit B. A few inches of malalignment in laying are permitted by this "socket and spigot" type of joint. When the hydraulic hooks are operated to pull unit A home into unit B, the taper will automatically correct the error of alignment (Fig. 70).

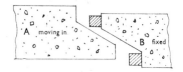

Fig. 70 Guiding in

But as soon as rubber-to-concrete contact is made we have a repetition of the problem of pent-up water pressure. The annular space S in Fig. 69 is now full of water, which cannot escape as the joint closes further. So again we need a bleed hole and valve which has the same two functions as the one shown in Fig. 66. It will have also a third purpose; for as soon as the rubber rings are compressed to their permissible maximum, cement grout can be pumped through a similar duct in the bottom of the section. The water in the space between the two gaskets will be forced out through the bleed hole (Fig. 69). This bleed will occur at the highest point of the tunnel section, so when grout appears at this valve we shall know that the space is completely filled with cement. When the cement has hardened, we can release all the water from the larger space between the diaphragms.

Closed

Closure of the joint is now complete, but before we can set about removing the diaphragms we must be sure that the joint cannot be disturbed.

There are three possible enemies of the safe watertight joint:—
1. Differential settlement of the foundations under the weight of the tunnel units.
2. Differential compaction of the screed caused by vibrations set up by trains passing through the tunnel.
3. Earthquakes

The first of these can be dismissed very quickly. The floor of the trench will be chalk. The chalk has been there for a long time, supporting without difficulty, and without movement, a far greater load then the tunnel will put upon it. For when digging the trench we shall have taken away a much greater weight than we shall be putting back. (Remember that the tunnel sections are hollow!). The gravel screed, however, is a different matter. It may settle a bit, but the way in which this happens is well understood and there is no doubt that the rubber joints can take care of far more foundation movement than is likely to happen from this cause. Indeed, the effect of movement, if any, will be so slight that minutely fractional adjustment of rail levels inside the tunnel would easily rectify it.

The second problem has been nullified by some complex mathematics allied to prolonged and very careful observations in an underwater railway tunnel in New York. Without delving into the algebra of harmonic motion, it might be explained that ground vibrations, like any other vibrations, consist of very small to-and-fro oscillations. The ground, over a large area, moves as a complete structure, and between each "to" and "fro" the speed of the movement changes with a varying acceleration. It is the maximum value of this acceleration, combined with the number of vibrations per second which determine whether a quake will damage a structure resting on or in the ground. In the New York tunnel it was found that the worst vibrations caused by the heaviest trains were only one-thirtieth of the vibrations which have to be allowed for, by law, when designing structures. So unless our Channel Tunnel locomotives produce vibrations thirty times as bad as the American engines—and this is not likely—we need not worry unduly about the Tunnel "slipping a disk."

What about earthquakes? These are only the same thing, but larger in amplitude (the distance from "to" to "fro" is two "amplitudes") and much slower. The English Channel is not in a severe earthquake zone.* The worst earthquake likely to occur in the region would not cause movements which could not be absorbed by the flexibility of the tunnel structure and the loose (non-rigid) material which will surround the slightly articulated tunnel units.

FILLETING

So, having satisfied ourselves that the joints are *permanently* closed, we can set about removing the diaphragms on each side of the joint between unit A and unit B in Fig. 66, p. 186. It is likely that at least one more tunnel unit will be laid (to the left of A) before the filleting begins, so that there will always be at least three watertight barriers between the sea and the men working inside the tunnel laying tracks, installing services—and removing the diaphragms themselves.

Now the difficulty of this task is dependent on the result of a design-stage war between convenience and cost. On the one hand, the diaphragms could be of concrete and expendable. That is to say they might have originally been installed as an integral part of the concrete structure. This would certainly simplify the construction work in the tube-casting yard. But it would mean that they would have to be cut out by pneumatic

---

*The Earth's surface is divided into earthquake "zones" by a series of numbers 1, 2, 3, ... according to the severity of quakes likely to occur.

hammer-drills in pieces small enough to be trucked out of the tunnel. This disposal of these waste lumps of concrete is, in itself, a major problem, unless some extensive shore-protection works happen to be going on nearby, where they could be used as anti-wave armour.

Alternatively, at the cost of some design headaches, it is possible to fabricate and install steel diaphragms, which can be removed by unbolting and folding, like the doors of telephone booths in railway stations. Making them in such a way that they could be dismantled in more than two parts would be uneconomical at the greater depths; a jointed diaphragm capable of withstanding thousands of tons of water pressure is not a nice prospect to structural engineers. We are left then with the task of transporting an enormously heavy steel structure for miles through

Fig. 71 Backfilling   Fig. 72 Backfilled

a tunnel in which all work would have to stop while they pass. This method has the advantage that the diaphragms could be used again in the casting yard, so offsetting the much higher cost of steel as a material of construction. Removable re-usable concrete diaphragms are not practicable; they would be just too heavy to handle out of the tunnel.

FILLING

The backfilling of the trench around the tunnel is yet another task, part of which can be put on the broad shoulders of platform No. 2. The bunkers on the platform deck (see Fig. 61, facing p. 177) will be kept replenished by a fleet of ships carrying sand and gravel. At the rear end of the platform will be installed a tremie pipe which will shoot the fine-grained material into the trench until the level of the fill has reached about half-way up the sides of the tunnel (Fig. 71). Halting at this level will leave access to the tunnel units if any inspection by diver is required. It will also permit the backfill to settle and consolidate more thoroughly than if the backfilling were completed in one operation. It is after this initial stage of backfilling, when the units can no longer move about on their screed bed that the pontoons will be finally removed.

At a later date, the trench will be topped up to sea-bed level, finishing with a slight hump (Fig. 72) to allow for final settlement to the dotted line. The top will be armoured with lumps of rock so large that they will not be moved by the fastest water currents likely to be generated by spring tides. The topping-up may possibly be done by walking the platform backwards during spells of bad weather when tube laying cannot proceed. But this would be a cumbersome movement and the advance planning of the platform's various movements and stockpiling of so many different types of material in its bunkers for several days ahead would be very complicated. It may prove to be more efficient to plan for the backfilling and armouring (large stones) to be done by floating craft, which could do this sort of work in almost any weather.

We now have behind us a long length of completed tunnel. The longer it becomes, the nearer we get to the English coast line and to our next major problem.

CHAPTER SIXTEEN

Land ahoy!

which refers to the problem of laying the tunnel in shallow water and linking up with the landward routes

THE END OF THE LONG WALK

THE WALKING platform will have started its long paddle at a point near the French coast.* Here its legs will have been comparatively short. As it strode into deeper water, the legs were lengthened by adding sections on top, until in mid-Channel the legs were more than 300 feet long. Then, as the Kent coast hove in sight, the legs were shortened again until we have now reached a depth of water in which the tunnel units can only just be floated out to the platform. And here our amiable monster must stop. But the trench bottom is still many feet below water level, and there is a gap between the Kent coast and the deep blue sea.

WADING OUT (OR IN)

However, in spite of the excitement of the new-style operations at sea, we have not forgotten everything else. Whilst the walking platforms were blazing the new trail from France towards England, a more conventional tunnel was being drilled from the portal behind Folkestone. The route of this subterranean tunnel (actually a pair of tunnels) follows very much the same route as that described on p. 121 and for the same reasons. It can turn south-eastwards towards the shoreline slightly earlier because it does not have to go so deep. By the time it reaches the shoreline it is of course well below ground level, for it is being bored by tunnelling moles and must remain in the Chalk. But at some stage the twin tunnel must venture out to sea to a rendezvous

---

*See p. 165. "Direction finding . . ."

with the platform-laid tube. The position now is shown in Fig. 73.

The orthodox next step would be to build a cofferdam ABCD from the cliffs to the end of the immersed tube, as shown in plan in Fig. 74. The end wall BC of this sheet-pile (or embankment) dam could fit snugly round the end of the tube F. Then the water inside the cofferdam could be pumped out and the remaining work of connecting the two tunnels would be a straightforward construction job on dry land.

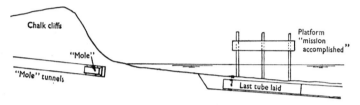

Fig. 73 Land ahoy!

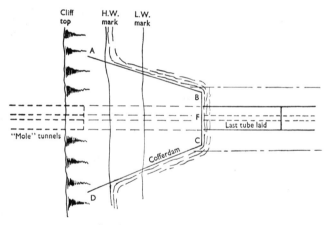

Fig. 74 Getting ashore

It might be, however, that a less sophisticated solution would combine simplicity with economic advantage. The space at the end of the trench could be filled with concrete which would engulf and seal the end of the immersed tube. Then the tunnel bore under the cliff could be simply continued out under the shore, through the concrete plug, until it broke out inside the immersed tube.   The ground under the shore may need a measure of consolidation grouting.

LOOKING BACK

It might be mentioned here that a somewhat similar cofferdam would be used on the French side in the very early stages.   Here, the end BC of the cofferdam would incorporate a diaphragm and "tube end" exactly similar to the leading end of one of the pre-fabricated tunnel units.   The first unit to be laid by the walking platform would be socketed into this cofferdam end wall and then the long cross-Channel walk could proceed.   Only in this way can we ensure access to the inside of the immersed tunnel for the heavy equipment which will be required there, for diaphragm removal, track laying, etc.

There would probably be no landward tunnel on the French side, since there are no cliffs and the shore conditions there would permit the concrete tunnel to come straight up out of the sea until it is above the water line.   The depth would then be so little that the final rise to ground level could be entirely in open cutting.

When the transition tunnels have crossed the sea shores, the sand will be replaced and the pleasures of building sandcastles and trips in the Saucy Sue will be restored to holiday makers. "You will never know it is there" and this book will be forgotten!

PART FOUR

Stop press

which is exactly what it says

What goes on?

READERS WHO are aware of the Government White Paper of September 1963 may have wondered why no mention of it was made in Chapter 3. It was in fact a very comprehensive document, but earlier mention of it in this book might have trailed some rather sophisticated red herrings across the path of the arguments presented in the subsequent chapters. Only two of its sixty pages are really relevant to what we have been talking about, although the rest of it provides a feast of interesting reading under the headings of traffic estimates, costs, economics, and finance.

In the very short section on "practicability" the Report states that the "project for a *bored* tunnel is acceptable from the engineering point of view, both in principle and in the design and method of construction proposed." It is considered "nevertheless that before the scheme were finally approved from the technical point of view a further geological survey would be necessary. This survey . . . . would need to be capable of revealing any local irregularities, such as faults or water-bearing pockets, likely to prevent the completion of the work." There is considerable confidence in the subsequent remark that "satisfactory results from this survey . . . . would virtually remove any risk that it might be physically impossible to complete the work." And a little further on: ". . . an immersed tunnel would not be likely to present serious geological problems and, if laid below the level of the sea-bed as proposed, the immersed tunnel would be protected from hazards due to shipping or tidal scour and would not be likely to have any effect on the regime of tides . . . . but the possible hazards during construction . . . . would need careful consideration."

---

*Proposals for a Fixed Channel Link. Min. of Transport, H.M.S.O., Cmnd. 2137.

These cautiously confident pronouncements are worded in a most precise manner and it is unfortunate that some non-technical journalists of the national Press did not thoroughly digest their implications before paraphrasing them in the dramatic way so beloved of Fleet Street. There have thus arisen several misconceptions about the "further geological survey."

The first of these is the belief that the undertaking of this survey indicates the rejection of the immersed tube proposals, since the Report appears to tie the survey to the comments on the bored tunnel. The second erroneous belief is that the geological survey may find "irregularities" which would make the bored tunnel impossible to achieve. There is no need here to add to the already long list of facetious definitions (which amount to disclaimers) of the word "impossible."

The commonest of all the misrepresentations, which is even quoted in the house bulletin of one of the contracting organizations most directly concerned, is that "Boring beneath the Channel will determine tunnel method."

And there are many other views that merely advertise the influence of the polemics which creep into public pronouncements by interested parties.

Let's get it straight. The "further geological survey" is aimed at getting positive attested evidence, from the sea-bed and below it, of the truth or otherwise of beliefs which have hitherto been merely *deduced* from available facts.

There is no question of the survey data being the sole determinant of the method to be adopted for building the Tunnel, or of being the criteria upon which one or other method will be rejected. The survey is a fact-finding mission. *After* tabulation, analysis, and discussion, the facts discovered *may* show that the problems to be faced in boring through the Lower Chalk or in digging a trench in the sea-bed will be either more or less severe and either more or less numerous than the planning engineers have so far allowed for. At the same time, the results of the survey will help to establish much more accurately than hitherto the best possible route for *either* a bored tunnel or an immersed tube.

And when all the facts have been co-ordinated the estimates

of cost and time of construction can be made more accurate and contingency allowances can be narrowed by amounts far exceeding the cost of the survey. All this is normal civil engineering preplanning procedure and it is only the enormous size of the job and its national importance which have given rise to the unstable corona of uninformed speculation which surrounds it.

So much for the reasons behind the "further geological survey," which actually started in the autumn of 1964. What is in fact going on?

The first stage of the exploratory work now being performed in the Channel consists in the drilling of boreholes, about $1\frac{1}{4}$ mile apart, in the sea-bed. They will reach down to depths ranging from 165 feet to 500 feet *below* the sea-bed and in every case cores will be extracted from as far down as the top of the Gault Clay. This will provide visual evidence of the characteristics of all the Chalk layers. A few of the boreholes will be taken right through the Gault into the Jurassic beds below. From the evidence of these preliminary boreholes it will be possible to determine the locations where even more accurate and detailed information, with special emphasis on porosity, would be of most use. Then a second series of boreholes will be driven to get this further information.

Simultaneously with the first series of boreholes, a geophysical survey, of the heavy-impulse type described on p. 99, will be made. The seismic information will be correlated with the borehole information to determine the most useful positions for the secondary boreholes, with microfossil data (see p. 101) from the primary cores providing accurate geographical control. The final tally of boreholes is likely to exceed seventy-five—a very considerable undertaking, but vital to the success of future operations.

The drilling work is being done by teams of British and French engineers working from converted tank landing craft. The survey is due to be completed in the autumn of 1965. Severe weather in the winter of 1964/5 has caused unexpected delays, but the engineers still hope to complete the drilling work within the contract time. When the results have been analysed and become available it is unlikely that they will provide any great shocks—or will they?

PERSONAL MESSAGE FROM AUTHOR

The labour of writing is ended. It has been a labour of love because I feel that a century in which there has been so much destruction of all that man holds dear should not come to its end without him being allowed to erect this greatest of all monuments to human endeavour and engineering skill.

There must be many who feel the same way without having previously understood the magnitude of the task. Its feasibility too has long been in doubt. It has been my object to spread a gospel far outside the coterie of engineers who alone have had a firm grasp of the difficulties involved in building the Channel Tunnel and faith in the practicality of their solutions.

There is now no doubt that the Tunnel is no pipe dream. What a pity it is that there remain the barriers of financial, legal, and political uncertainties. Public opinion cannot, of course, affect the validity of engineers' technological dicta, but it can and should help to put all the other impedimenta into their right perspective.

If this book has helped to widen, by a small fraction, the basis on which public opinion is formed, I shall be well rewarded. At the same time I am conscious that a great deal has been omitted. There are many details—such as cross-overs in the tunnel; terminal-area layout; signalling, lighting, and ventilation details; and so on—for which space could not be found in these pages. That may be a good thing in one way, for if I leave you nothing to question, nothing to think about, you will lay this book aside two minutes from now and forget about it. That would be a pity because I believe that informed public opinion may eventually have a major part to play in persuading the powers that be to let the engineers get on with the job.

Finally, I hope I have at least partly fulfilled the implied promise in the last paragraph of my Preface—that part of a book which so few ever read.

SUBJECT GUIDE

This is a technical book for the layman, not a text book on engineering. The latter is used for study and reference and a fully detailed index is essential. The reference index has no place here, but so many people look at the end of a book first, that the following list of headings and sub-headings may provide the incentive to start at the beginning.

Part I.   Once Upon A Time

Part II.   A Boring Tale

Part IV.   Stop Press